JUNIOR CYCL

LESS STRESS MORE SUCCESS

Maths Revision
Higher Level
Book 1

Number Strand and Algebra and Functions Strand

Brendan Guildea & Louise Boylan

GILL EDUCATION

Gill Education
Hume Avenue
Park West
Dublin 12
www.gilleducation.ie

Gill Education is an imprint of M.H. Gill & Co.

978 07171 9068 3

Print origination: MPS Limited
Artwork: MPS Limited, Andriy Yankovskyy

For permission to reproduce photographs, the authors and publisher gratefully
acknowledge the following:
© Alamy: 181; © iStock/Getty Premium: vii, 64, 72, 73, 74, 96, 97, 108, 146, 156,
172, 199, 199, 216, 218, 219, 221, 226; © Shutterstock: 83, 111, 217.

The authors and publisher have made every effort to trace all copyright holders. If,
however, any have been inadvertently overlooked, we would be pleased to make the
necessary arrangement at the first opportunity.

Acknowledgements

The authors would like to thank Carol Guildea, Joe Heron and Jack Mahon who
helped with the proofreading, checked the answers and made valuable suggestions that
are included in the final text.

CONTENTS

Please note:

The exam questions marked by the symbol ![exam Q] in this book are selected from the following:

1. SEC exam papers
2. Sample exam papers
3. Original and sourced exam-type questions

Introduction

aims

☐ To learn how to revise most effectively.
☐ To familiarise yourself with the four elements of assessment.
☐ To learn how to allocate the correct time for each question.
☐ To know and understand the words which appear often on the exam paper.
☐ To familiarise yourself with the syllabus.

The aim of this revision book is to help you get as high a mark as possible in your Junior Cycle Higher Level maths course. This book is designed to be exam focused and can be used in conjunction with **any** textbook.

Graded examples and exam questions

Throughout this book, **examples and exam-type questions are graded by level of difficulty**.

This level of difficulty is indicated by calculator symbols, as follows:

The number of calculators shown beside a question helps you know how difficult the question is. One calculator indicates a question which is relatively basic. As the questions get harder, the symbol will have more calculators. Three calculators will indicate an average-level question, whereas five calculators indicate that it is a very challenging question. These questions may be beyond some students, but give them a go! **Students hoping to achieve a high grade should aim to complete all of the 'five calculator' questions. The calculator symbol given for each question relates to the most difficult part of that question. It is important to not be discouraged by a challenging question.** In the Junior Cycle exam, difficult questions can sometimes begin with one or two simple parts; you should attempt as much as you can.

Preparing for your Junior Cycle Maths exam

It is very important to realise that **you are your own best teacher**. Revision is when you begin to teach yourself. Thus, it is very important for you to start your revision as soon as possible. Make notes while you are revising. If you are having difficulty with a particular question, seek help from your teacher, a friend or a member of your family. As with all subjects, the best examination preparation is to work through past examination or sample papers so that you are familiar with the layout and style of questions.

So let's start at the beginning. If you want to do well in your Junior Cycle Mathematics, then two things are essential:

- Revise effectively
- Be familiar with the exam paper and so be prepared on the day of the exam

These may seem obvious, but it's worth taking a moment to think about what these tips mean.

How to revise most effectively

If you are going to do well in the Junior Cycle, you are going to spend quite a bit of time revising. Spending a little time learning how to revise effectively will help you get more from your time and help you absorb and understand more of the material on the course. Here are some tips to help you revise for maths.

- Find a quiet place where you can work. This place should be dedicated to study, free of potential distractions. Turn off all music, the TV, computer and mobile phone.
- Draw up a study plan. Don't be afraid to ask your parents/teachers/guidance counsellor for help at this stage.
- Do the more challenging revision first, when you are fresh. Trying to focus on difficult problems when you are tired can be counter-productive.
- Your maths course is based on understanding, so while you can 'learn' some elements of the course, it is important that you develop an understanding of the material.
- Drill and practice are essential ingredients for success in maths.
- Try to link any new material to things you know already. This is learning through association and helps long-term retention.

Study in small chunks of time lasting 25 to 35 minutes. Your memory and concentration will work better if you study in short bursts, but often.

Don't get hung up on more difficult material. Concentrate on understanding the fundamental concepts and being able to answer all of the straightforward questions. Then, with time, you can build up to the more challenging problems.

Junior Cycle Maths Assessment

Your assessment in Junior Cycle Mathematics consists of four elements. We will look at these four elements in detail and in the order in which you will be completing them.

Classroom-Based Assessment 1 (CBA 1) – Mathematical Investigation (during second year)

Format: A report may be presented in a wide range of formats.

Preparation: A student will, over a three-week period in second year, follow the Problem-Solving Cycle to investigate a mathematical problem.

The Problem-Solving Cycle is as follows:

1. Define a problem
2. Decompose it into manageable parts and/or simplify it using appropriate assumptions
3. Translate the problem to mathematics, if necessary
4. Engage with the problem and solve it, if possible
5. Interpret any findings in the context of the original problem

The Problem-Solving Cycle

1. Define the problem
2. Breakdown the problem into parts
3. Translate the problem into maths
4. Engage with and solve the problem
5. Interpret findings

Assessment: The CBA is assessed by the class teacher.
A student will be awarded one of the following categories of achievement:

- Yet to meet expectations
- In line with expectations
- Above expectations
- Exceptional

Classroom-Based Assessment 2 (CBA 2) – Statistical Investigation (during third year)

Format: A report may be presented in a wide range of formats.

Preparation: A student will, over a three-week period in third year, follow the Statistical-Enquiry Cycle to investigate a mathematical problem.

The Statistical-Enquiry Cycle is as follows:

1. Formulate a question
2. Plan and collect unbiased, representative data
3. Organise and manage the data
4. Explore and analyse the data, using appropriate displays and numerical summaries
5. Answer the original question, giving reasons based on the analysis section

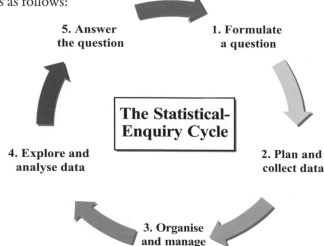

The Statistical-Enquiry Cycle

1. Formulate a question
2. Plan and collect data
3. Organise and manage the data
4. Explore and analyse data
5. Answer the question

Assessment: The CBA is assessed by the class teacher.
A student will be awarded one of the following categories of achievement:

- Yet to meet expectations
- In line with expectations
- Above expectations
- Exceptional

Assessment Task (during third year, after CBA 2)

Format: The Assessment Task is a specified written task, completed by students during class time.

Preparation: The Assessment Task is specified by the NCCA and is related to the learning outcomes on which CBA 2, the Statistical Investigation, is based.

Assessment: The Assessment Task is corrected by qualified teachers, as assigned by the SEC. The assessment task is allocated 10% of the marks used to determine the grade awarded by the SEC in Junior Cycle Mathematics.

The written exam paper (end of third year)

Format: A two-hour written exam, taking place at the end of third year.

Assessment: The exam is corrected by qualified teachers, as assigned by the SEC. The written exam is allocated 90% of the marks used to determine the grade awarded by the SEC in Junior Cycle Mathematics.

Read the exam paper right through at the start to determine which question is the easiest one to start with. Your mind may also be subconsciously processing some of the other problems.

Attempt marks are valuable, so it is vital that you attempt all questions.

Leave **NO** blanks.

Further exam tips

- There is no such thing as rough work in maths – all work is relevant. If the examiner doesn't know how you reached an answer, even a correct answer, then full marks will usually not be awarded. Thus, **show all your work**.

- It is a good idea to show each stage of a calculation when using a calculator (in case you press a wrong key). **Familiarise yourself with your calculator. Know your book of tables and formulae well and write down any formula that you use.**

Your calculator and book of tables are two extremely valuable resources to have in the exam. Make sure that you are very familiar with how your calculator works and that you know how to perform all functions on it. Also familiarise yourself with the book of tables so that you don't waste any time in the exam trying to find formulae.

- Attempt marks (partial credit) will be awarded for any step in the right direction. Therefore, **make an attempt at each part of the question**. Even if you do not get the correct answer, you can still pick up most of the marks on offer if you show how you worked it out. Also, **draw a diagram where possible** because this can help in seeing the solution.

- If you cannot finish part of a question, leave a space and come back to it later. **Never scribble out any work or use Tipp-Ex.** Put a single line through it so that the examiner can still read it. **Avoid using pencil** because the writing can be very faint and difficult to read.

- **Do not judge the length of your answer based on the size of the space provided.** Sometimes large spaces are provided for questions where only a short solution is required.

- If you run out of space in your answer booklet, **ask the supervisor for more paper**. Then clearly write the number of the exam question and the solution on the extra paper.

Glossary of common phrases used throughout your Mathematics course and on the examination paper

Analyse, Investigate
Observe, study or examine something in detail, in order to establish facts and reach new conclusions.

Apply, Use
Select and use knowledge, skills or rules to put theory into practice and solve a problem.

Calculate, Find, Determine
Obtain your answers by showing all relevant work. Marks are available for showing the steps leading to your final answer or conclusion.

Classify
Group things based on common characteristics.

Comment on, Discuss, Interpret
After studying the given information or your answers, give your opinion on their significance. Use your knowledge and understanding to explain the meaning of something in context.

Compare
Give an account of the similarities and (or) differences between two (or more) items or situations, referring to both (all) of them throughout.

Construct
Draw an accurate diagram, usually labelled, using a pencil, ruler, set square, compass and protractor. Leave all constructions on your diagram.

Convert
Change from one form to another.

Estimate
State or calculate a rough value for a particular quantity.

Evaluate
Usually to work out, or find, a numerical value by putting in numbers for letters.

Explain, Show that, Prove, Verify, Justify
Demonstrate that a statement is true. This could be a given statement or to be able to show that your answer is correct.

Give your answer in the form ...
This means the examiner wants the final answer in a particular form, for example, as a fraction, in surd form, in index notation, rounded to a particular number of decimal places, etc. Watch out for this, as your will lose marks if your answer is not in the correct form.

Generalise
Generate a general statement, based on specific instance.

Generate
To produce or create.

Hence
You *must* use the answer, or result, from the previous part of the question.

Hence or otherwise
It is recommended that you use the answer, or result, from the previous part of the question, but other methods are acceptable.

Mathematise
Generate a mathematical representation (e.g. graph, equation, geometric figure) to describe a particular aspect of a phenomenon.

Plot
Indicate the position of points on a graph, usually on the x- and y-planes.

Sketch
Make a rough diagram or graph, labelled if needed.

Solve
Find the solution, or root, of an equation. The solution is the value of the variable that makes the left-hand side balance with the right-hand side.

Understand
Have detailed knowledge of, be able to use appropriately, and see the connections between parts.

Write down, State
You can write down your answer without showing any work. However, if you want you can show some workings.

Syllabus checklist for Junior Cycle Higher Level Maths: Number Strand and Algebra and Functions Strand

Throughout your course you will be asked to apply your knowledge and skills to solve problems in familiar and unfamiliar contexts. In problem solving, you should use some of the following strategies.

- Trial and improvement
- Draw a diagram
- Look for a pattern
- Act it out
- Draw a table
- Simplify the problem
- Use an equation
- Work backwards
- Eliminate possibilities

The syllabus stresses that in all aspects of the Junior Cycle maths course, you should be able to:

☐ Explore patterns and formulate conjectures.

☐ Explain findings.

☐ Justify conclusions.

☐ Communicate mathematics verbally and in written form.

☐ Apply your knowledge and skills to solve problems in familiar and unfamiliar contexts.

☐ Analyse information presented verbally and translate it into mathematical form.

☐ Devise, select and use appropriate mathematical models, formulae or techniques to process information and to draw relevant conclusions.

Unifying strand

Throughout the Junior Cycle maths course, students should develop the skills associated with each of the following elements:

Building blocks

Students should understand and recall the concepts that underpin each strand, and be able to carry out the resulting procedures accurately, effectively, and appropriately.

Representation

Students should be able to represent a mathematical situation in a variety of different ways and translate flexibly between them.

Connections

Students should be able to make connections within strands and between strands, as well as connections between mathematics and the real world.

Problem solving

Students should be able to investigate patterns, formulate conjectures, and engage in tasks in which the solution is not immediately obvious, in familiar and unfamiliar contexts.

Generalisation and proof

Students should be able to move from specific instances to general mathematical statements, and to present and evaluate mathematical arguments and proofs.

Communication

Students should be able to communicate mathematics effectively in verbal and written form.

Number systems

- [ ] Understand the different types of numbers
  - ○ $\mathbb{N}$: the set of natural numbers $\{1, 2, 3, 4, ...\}$
  - ○ $\mathbb{Z}$: the set of integers, including 0
  - ○ $\mathbb{Q}$: the set of rational numbers
  - ○ $\mathbb{R}$: the set of real numbers
  - ○ $\mathbb{R}\backslash\mathbb{Q}$: the set of irrational numbers
- [ ] Represent the operations of addition, subtraction, multiplication, and division in $\mathbb{N}$, $\mathbb{Z}$, and $\mathbb{Q}$ using models including the number line, decomposition, and accumulating groups of equal size.
- [ ] Perform the operations of addition, subtraction, multiplication, and division and understand the relationship between these operations and the properties: commutative, associative and distributive in $\mathbb{N}$, $\mathbb{Z}$, and $\mathbb{Q}$ and in $\mathbb{R}\backslash\mathbb{Q}$, including operating on surds
- [ ] Calculate and interpret factors (including the highest common factor), multiples (including the lowest common multiple), and prime numbers.
- [ ] Present numerical answers to the degree of accuracy specified, for example, correct to the nearest hundred, to two decimal places, or to three significant figures.
- [ ] Flexibly convert between fractions, decimals, and percentages.

Expressions

- [ ] Investigate situations in which letters stand for quantities that are variable.
- [ ] Generate and interpret expressions in which letters stand for numbers.
- [ ] Find the value of expressions given the value of the variables.
- [ ] Use the concept of equality to generate and interpret equations.
- [ ] Add, subtract and simplify
  - ○ linear expressions in one or more variables with coefficients in $\mathbb{Q}$
  - ○ quadratic expressions in one variable with coefficients in $\mathbb{Z}$
  - ○ expressions of the form $\dfrac{a}{bx + c}$, where $a, b, c \in \mathbb{Z}$
- [ ] Multiply expressions of the form
  - ○ $a(bx + cy + d)$
  - ○ $a(bx^2 + cx + d)$
  - ○ $ax(bx^2 + cx + d)$, where $a, b, c, d \in \mathbb{Z}$
  - ○ $(ax + b)(cx + d)$
  - ○ $(ax + b)(cx^2 + dx + e)$, where $a, b, c, d, e \in \mathbb{Z}$
- [ ] Divide quadratic and cubic expressions by linear expressions, where all coefficients are integers and there is no remainder.

☐ Flexibly convert between the factorised and expanded forms of algebraic expressions of the form:

- ○ axy, where $a \in \mathbb{Z}$
- ○ $axy + byz$, where $a, b \in \mathbb{Z}$
- ○ $sx - ty + tx - sy$, where $s, t \in \mathbb{Z}$
- ○ $dx^2 + bx$
- ○ $ax^2 + bx + c$, where $b, c, d \in \mathbb{Z}$ and $a \in \mathbb{N}$
- ○ $a^2x^2 - b^2y^2$, where $a, b \in \mathbb{Z}$

☐ Apply the relationship between operations and an understanding of the order of operations including brackets and exponents to change the subject of a formula.

Equations and inequalities

☐ Select and use suitable strategies (graphic, numeric, algebraic, trial and improvement, working backwards) for finding solutions to:

- ○ linear equations in one variable with coefficients in $\mathbb{Q}$ and solutions in $\mathbb{Z}$ or in $\mathbb{Q}$
- ○ quadratic equations in one variable with coefficients and solutions in $\mathbb{Z}$ or coefficients in $\mathbb{Q}$ and solutions in $\mathbb{R}$
- ○ simultaneous linear equations in two variables with coefficients and solutions in $\mathbb{Z}$ or in $\mathbb{Q}$
- ○ linear inequalities in one variable of the form $g(x) < k$, and graph the solution sets on the number line for $x \in \mathbb{N}, \mathbb{Z},$ and $\mathbb{R}$
- ○ Generate quadratic equations given integer roots.

Indices

☐ Flexibly translate between whole numbers and index representation of numbers.

☐ Use and apply rules for indices.

☐ Understand binary operations of addition, subtraction, multiplication and division in the context of numbers in index form.

☐ Correctly use the order of arithmetic and index operations including the use of brackets.

☐ Generalise numerical relationships involving operations involving numbers written in index form.

☐ Operate on the set of irrational numbers $\mathbb{R}\backslash\mathbb{Q}$.

☐ Convert the number p in decimal form to the form $a \times 10^n$, where $1 \le a < 10$, $n \in \mathbb{Z}, p \in \mathbb{Q},$ and $p \ge 1$ and $0 < p < 1$.

Patterns

☐ Analyse numerical patterns in different ways, including making out tables and graphs, and continue such patterns.

☐ Investigate patterns and relationships (linear, quadratic, doubling and tripling) in numbers, spatial patterns and real-world phenomena involving change.

☐ Be able to represent patterns and relationships in tables and graphs.

☐ Generate a generalised expression for linear and quadratic patterns in words and algebraic expressions and fluently convert between each representation.

☐ Categorise patterns as linear, non-linear, quadratic, and exponential (doubling and tripling) using their defining characteristics as they appear in the different representations..

Sets

☐ Understand the concept of a set as a well-defined collection of elements.

☐ Understand that set equality is a relationship where two sets have the same elements.

☐ Define sets by listing their elements, if finite (including in a 2-set or 3-set Venn diagram), or by generating rules that define them.

☐ Use and understand suitable set notation and terminology, including null set, $\varnothing$, subset, complement, element, $\in$, universal set, cardinal number, #, intersection, $\cap$, union, $\cup$, set difference, $\setminus$, $\mathbb{N}$, $\mathbb{Z}$, $\mathbb{Q}$, $\mathbb{R}$, and $\mathbb{R}\setminus\mathbb{Q}$.

☐ Perform the following operations on 2 sets and on 3 sets

   ○ intersection

   ○ union (for three sets)

   ○ set difference

   ○ complement

☐ Be able to use brackets with set notation, to define the order of operations.

☐ Investigate whether the set operations of intersection, union, and difference are commutative and/or associative.

Functions

☐ Demonstrate understanding of the concept of a function.

☐ Represent and interpret functions in different ways:

   ○ graphically (for $x \in \mathbb{N}$, $\mathbb{Z}$, and $\mathbb{R}$, [continuous functions only], as appropriate)

   ○ diagrammatically

   ○ in words

   ○ algebraically

   ○ use the language and notation of functions (domain, range, co-domain, $f(x) =$, $f : x \longmapsto$, and $y =$)

☐ Use graphical methods to find and interpret approximate solutions of equations such as $f(x) = g(x)$ and approximate solution sets of inequalities such as $f(x) < g(x)$.

☐ Make connections between the shape of a graph and the story of a phenomenon, including identifying and interpreting maximum and minimum points.

Applied measure

☐ Calculate, interpret and apply units of measure and time.

☐ Solve problems that involve calculating average speed, distance and time.

Applied arithmetic

☐ Making value for money calculations and judgements.

☐ Use and understand ratio and proportion.

☐ Solve money-related problems that involve:

- bills
- currency conversion
- VAT
- profit or loss
- percentage profit or loss
- cost price
- selling price
- mark-up
- margin
- compound interest
- income tax
- net pay (including other deductions)

☐ Investigate situations involving proportionality so you can use absolute and relative comparison where appropriate.

☐ Solve problems involving proportionality including those involving:

- currency conversion
- average speed, distance, and time

1   Number Systems

aims

☐ To learn what the symbols ℕ, ℤ, ℚ, ℝ\ℚ and ℝ represent.

☐ To be familiar with prime numbers, factors and the fundamental theorem of arithmetic.

☐ To be able to find LCM and HCF as required.

☐ To have a clear understanding of and be able to complete calculations using the order of operations.

Number sets

Four of the five number sets required on our course are to be found in the booklet of formulae and tables. It gives us:

Number sets

$\mathbb{N} = \{1, 2, 3, 4, 5, 6, \cdots\}$ Natural numbers

$\mathbb{Z} = \{\cdots -3, -2, -1, 0, 1, 2, 3, \cdots\}$ Integers

$\mathbb{Q} = \left\{ \dfrac{p}{q} \middle| p \in \mathbb{Z}, \quad q \in \mathbb{Z}, \quad q \neq 0 \right\}$ Rational numbers

$\mathbb{R}$ Real numbers

The set not given in the tables is the set of irrational numbers, represented by ℝ\ℚ.

We meet the set of irrational numbers later in this chapter.

A Venn diagram of the number system looks like this:

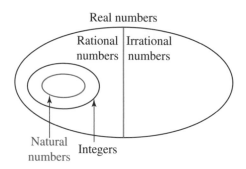

Natural numbers ℕ

The positive whole numbers 1, 2, 3, 4, 5 . . . are also called the counting numbers. The dots indicate that the numbers go on forever and have no end (infinite).

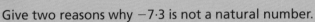

exam Q

Give two reasons why -7.3 is not a natural number.

Solution

Reason 1: It is a negative number.

Reason 2: It is not a whole number (it is a decimal).

Factors (divisors)

key point

The factors of any whole number are the whole numbers that divide exactly into the given number, leaving no remainder.

- 1 is a factor of every number.
- Every number is a factor of itself.

Example

Find the factors of 18.
Find the factors of 45.
Hence find the highest common factor of 18 and 45.

Solution

18	45
1×18	1×45
2×9	3×15
3×6	5×9

The common factors are 1, 3 and 9.

$\therefore$ The highest common factor of 18 and 45 is 9.

key point

The highest common factor (HCF) of two or more numbers is the largest factor that is common to each of the given numbers.

Example

In these productogons, the number in each square is the product of the numbers in the circles on each side of it. Find the missing numbers in each of these productogons.

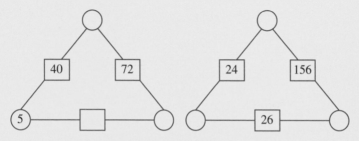

Solution

The use of the word productogon in the question indicates we use multiplication. This is because product means multiply.

This first one is very straightforward.

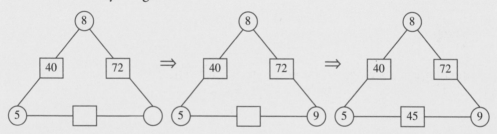

The second one is more challenging.

The method of trial and improvement (yes, guesswork!) is used here. Of the three given numbers, 24 and 26 would seem to have the easiest factors for us to find.

24	26
1×24	1×26
2×12	2×13
3×8	
4×6	

This indicates the bottom left-hand number is either 1 or 2, as they are the only factors common to both 24 and 26.

Let's put 1 into the bottom left-hand corner:

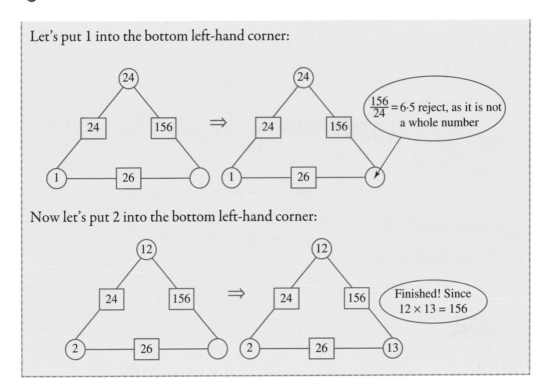

Now let's put 2 into the bottom left-hand corner:

Prime numbers

A prime number is a whole number greater than 1 that has only two factors, 1 and itself.

The first 12 prime numbers are

2, 3, 5, 7, 11, 13, 17, 19, 23, 29, 31 and 37.

There is an infinite number of prime numbers.

Numbers that have more than two factors are called composite numbers.

The first 12 composite numbers are 4, 6, 8, 9, 10, 12, 14, 15, 16, 18, 20 and 21. There is an infinite number of composite numbers.

The fundamental theorem of arithmetic states that any whole number greater than 1 can be written as the product of its prime factors in a **unique** way. This will underpin many exam questions on number theory.

Prime factors

Any number can be expressed as a product of prime numbers. To express the number 180 as a product of its prime numbers, first divide by the smallest prime number that will divide exactly into it.

The smallest prime number 2 :	2	180
The smallest prime 2 again :	2	90
The smallest prime 3 :	3	45
The smallest prime 3 again :	3	15
The smallest prime 5 :	5	5
		1

So 180 expressed as a product of primes is $2 \times 2 \times 3 \times 3 \times 5 = 2^2 \times 3^2 \times 5$.

Example

For security, a credit card is encrypted using prime factors. A huge number is assigned to each individual card and it can only be verified by its prime factor decomposition. Find the 10-digit natural number which is assigned to the following credit cards whose prime factor decomposition is

(i) $2 \times 3 \times 11 \times 13 \times 17^2 \times 19^3$

(ii) $2^7 \times 3^2 \times 5^2 \times 7^3 \times 23 \times 31$

Solution

By calculator   (i) 1700771358

                (ii) 7043299200

Example

Geppetto makes wooden puppets. He has four lengths of wood which he wants to cut into pieces, all of which must be the same length and be as long as possible. The lengths of the four pieces of wood are 315 cm, 357 cm, 210 cm and 252 cm.

 (i) Express each of the four lengths as a product of primes.

(ii) Hence, calculate what length each piece should be and how many pieces he will have.

Solution

(i)

```
3|315        3|357        2|210        2|252
3|105        7|119        3|105        2|126
5|35        17|17         5|35         3|63
7|7          |1           7|7          3|21
 |1                        |1          7|7
                                        |1
```

$3^2 \times 5 \times 7$ $3 \times 7 \times 17$ $2 \times 3 \times 5 \times 7$ $2^2 \times 3^2 \times 7$

(ii) By observation of the four 'products of primes' above:

The highest common factor (HCF) is given by
$3 \times 7 = 21$.

Hence, each piece of wood should be 21 cm long.

key point

3 × 7 is common to all four lengths.

The number of pieces is given by
$$\frac{315}{21} + \frac{357}{21} + \frac{210}{21} + \frac{252}{21}$$

$$= 15 + 17 + 10 + 12$$

$$= 54$$

Integers $\mathbb{Z}$

Negative numbers are numbers below zero. Positive and negative **whole** numbers including 0 are called integers.

Integers can be represented on a number line:

Integers to the right of zero are called **positive integers**.
Integers to the left of zero are called **negative integers**.

Example

At midnight on Christmas Eve the temperatures in some cities were as shown in the table.

(i) Which city recorded the
  (a) Lowest temperature
  (b) Highest temperature?
(ii) List the temperatures from coldest to hottest.
(iii) Which cities had a temperature difference of 6°C?
(iv) What is the difference in temperature between
  (a) Dublin and Moscow
  (b) Cairo and Dublin?

New York	2°C
Rome	−2°C
Dublin	−1°C
Moscow	−20°C
Cairo	4°C

Solution

(i) (a) Lowest temperature, −20°, in Moscow
    (b) Highest temperature, 4°, in Cairo
(ii) −20, −2, −1, 2, 4
(iii)

Rome and Cairo had a difference of 6°C.

(iv) (a) Dublin and Moscow $= -1 - (-20) = -1 + 20 = 19°$
     (b) Cairo and Dublin $= 4 - (-1) = 4 + 1 = 5°$

Multiplication and division of two integers

The following two rules are applied to the multiplication or division of two integers.

1. If the signs are the same, then the answer will be positive.

e.g. $\dfrac{-10}{-2} = +5; \quad (-10)(-2) = +20; \quad \dfrac{+10}{+2} = +5$

2. If the signs are different, then the answer will be negative.

e.g. $\dfrac{-10}{+2} = -5; \quad (+10)(-2) = -20; \quad \dfrac{+10}{-2} = -5$

Example

Find the missing number in each box.

(i) $\square \times 5 = -10$ (ii) $8 \times \square = -24$

(iii) $-12 \div \square = 4$ (iv) $\square \div -9 = -4$

Solution

(i) $\square \times 5 = -10$

$$\square = \frac{-10}{5}$$

$$\square = -2$$

(ii) $8 \times \square = -24$

$$\square = \frac{-24}{8}$$

$$\square = -3$$

(iii) $-12 \div \square = 4$

$$\frac{-12}{\square} = 4$$

$$-12 = 4\square$$

$$\frac{-12}{4} = \square$$

$$-3 = \square$$

(iv) $\square \div -9 = -4$

$$\frac{\square}{-9} = -4$$

$$\square = (-4)(-9)$$

$$\square = 36$$

Order of operations

A memory aid for the order of operations is BEMDAS (brackets, exponents, multiplication and division, addition and subtraction).

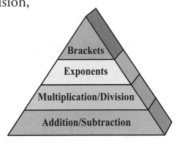

Order of operations

key point

Exponent(s) = Power(s) = Index (indices)

Brackets

Exponents

Multiplication/Division

Addition/Subtraction

Example

Calculate: (i) $8 + 108 \div -9$ (ii) $10 \times 4 - 30 \div 6 + 19$

Solution

(i) $8 + 108 \div -9$

$= 8 - 12$ Division

$= -4$ Subtraction

(ii) $10 \times 4 - 30 \div 6 + 19$

$= 40 - 30 \div 6 + 19$ Multiplication

$= 40 - 5 + 19$ Division

$= 59 - 5$ Addition

$= 54$ Subtraction

Example

Calculate $4(5 - 3)^2 + 24 \div (6 - 2)$.

Solution

$$4(5 - 3)^2 + 24 \div (6 - 2)$$
$$= 4(2)^2 + 24 \div 4 \qquad \text{Brackets}$$
$$= 4(4) + 24 \div 4 \qquad \text{Exponents/powers}$$
$$= 16 + 24 \div 4 \qquad \text{Multiplication}$$
$$= 16 + 6 \qquad \text{Division}$$
$$= 22 \qquad \text{Addition}$$

exam focus

Remember to confirm your answer with a calculator.

Fractions

A fraction is written as two whole numbers, one over the other, separated by a bar.

key point

$$\text{Fraction} = \frac{\text{Numerator}}{\text{Denominator}}$$

Equivalent fractions are fractions that are equal. For example:

$$\frac{1}{3} = \frac{2}{6} = \frac{3}{9} = \frac{4}{12}$$

This can be shown on a diagram where the same proportion is shaded in each circle.

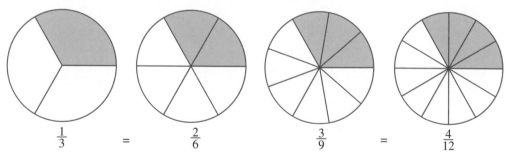

$\frac{1}{3}$ $\qquad =$ $\qquad \frac{2}{6}$ $\qquad\qquad \frac{3}{9}$ $\qquad =$ $\qquad \frac{4}{12}$

key point

The order of operations, BEMDAS, for fractions is the same as for integers.

Example

Bren is trying to subtract $\frac{1}{5}$ from $\frac{7}{8}$.

His attempt is shown here: $\frac{7}{8} - \frac{1}{5} = \frac{6}{3} = 2$

(i) Explain what Bren has done wrong.

(ii) Write out the correct solution.

Solution

(i) It seems that Bren has subtracted top from top and bottom from bottom.

key point

> For subtraction or addition of fractions, we must find a common denominator.

(ii) $\frac{7}{8} - \frac{1}{5} \Rightarrow$ common denominator $= 8 \times 5 = 40$

$$\text{Then } \frac{7}{8} - \frac{1}{5} = \frac{(5)(7) - (8)(1)}{40} = \frac{35 - 8}{40} = \frac{27}{40}$$

exam Q

(i) The diagram below shows three-fifths of a rectangle.
Complete the rectangle on the grid.

(ii) By shading appropriate sections of the strips below, show that

$$\frac{1}{3} + \frac{2}{6} \neq \frac{3}{9}$$

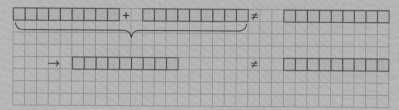

Solution

(i) By counting the rows (6) and the columns (12), the area of the given rectangle equals 6 × 12 = 72 square units.

This tells us that $\frac{3}{5}$ of the rectangle = 72 square units.

$$\Rightarrow \frac{1}{5} \text{ of the rectangle} = \frac{72}{3} = 24 \text{ square units.}$$

We conclude the full rectangle = 24 × 5 = 120 square units.

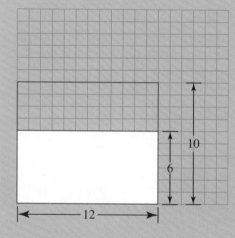

Many candidates simply counted 6 units (boxes) in height and since $\frac{6}{10} = \frac{3}{5}$ they wrote down the height of the full rectangle as 10 units (boxes) (see diagram).

(ii) $\frac{1}{3} + \frac{2}{6} \neq \frac{3}{9}$

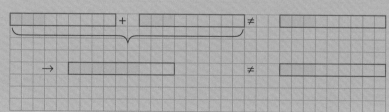

$$\frac{2}{6} = \frac{1}{3}$$

(a) (i) Write the numbers 3, 9, and 25 into the three empty boxes shown to make the mathematical statement true. Use each number only once.

(ii) Write the numbers 3, 5, 9, and 25 into the empty boxes shown so that the difference between the two fractions is as large as possible. Use each number only once.

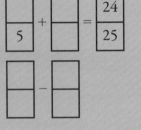

(b) A positive whole number has exactly 4 factors. One of the factors is 9. Work out the number.

Solution

(a) (i) The result of $\frac{24}{25}$ is less than one, so both fractions on the left side must both be less than one. This means that the number 3 must go above the 5. And for the second fraction, the 9 must be above the 25. You can verify your answer using your calculator.

$$\frac{3}{5} + \frac{9}{25} = \frac{24}{25}$$

(ii) To make the difference as large as possible, the first fraction needs to be as large as possible and the second fraction needs to be as small as possible. To make a fraction large – make the numerator big and the denominator small. To make a fraction small – make the numerator small and the denominator big. To make the difference as large as possible, we need to arrange the numbers in the fractions as shown:

$$\frac{25}{3} - \frac{5}{9}$$

(b) Since one of the factors of the required number is 9, we know that the number we are looking for is a multiple of 9. We need to examine the multiples of 9 and see how many factors they have. The first one we find that has 4 factors will be a correct answer.

Multiple	Factors	Number of factors	
9	1, 9	2	✗
18	1, 2, 3, 6, 9, 18	6	✗
27	1, 3, 9, 27	4	✓

So, the answer is 27.

Fractions (rational numbers, ℚ) are the third set of numbers listed in the booklet of formulae and tables. The set ℚ contains all the integers ℤ, which in turn contains all the natural numbers ℕ. You must know this.

The Venn diagram at the beginning of this chapter should help you understand this exam focus.

Irrational numbers

The word 'irrational' literally means 'no ratio'. Numbers which cannot be written as simple fractions are called irrational numbers (cannot be written as one integer divided by another integer). As decimals, they never repeat or terminate.

Using your calculator to evaluate $\sqrt{3}$ and π gives:

$$\sqrt{3} = 1 \cdot 732050808 \qquad \text{(irrational, never repeats or terminates)}$$
$$\pi = 3 \cdot 141592654 \ldots \qquad \text{(irrational, never repeats or terminates)}$$

The popular approximation of $\pi = \dfrac{22}{7} = 3 \cdot 142857143 \ldots$ is close but not accurate.

We use the set notation $\mathbb{R} \backslash \mathbb{Q}$ for irrational numbers.

key point

A rational number cannot be an irrational number and an irrational number cannot be a rational number.

Real numbers ℝ

When rational numbers and irrational numbers are joined together, they form a set of numbers called the real numbers ℝ.

The following Venn diagram summarises the number system.

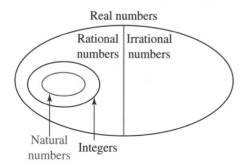

key point

Natural numbers are a subset of the integers. The integers are a subset of the rational numbers.

(i) The columns in the table below represent the following sets of numbers:

Natural numbers ($\mathbb{N}$), integers ($\mathbb{Z}$), rational numbers ($\mathbb{Q}$),

irrational numbers ($\mathbb{R}\backslash\mathbb{Q}$) and real numbers ($\mathbb{R}$).

Complete the table by writing either 'Yes' or 'No' into each box, indicating whether each of the numbers $\sqrt{5}$, 8, -4, $3\frac{1}{2}$, $\frac{3\pi}{4}$ is or is not an element of each.

(One box has already been filled in. The 'Yes' indicates that the number 8 is an element of the set of real numbers, $\mathbb{R}$.)

Number/Set	$\mathbb{N}$	$\mathbb{Z}$	$\mathbb{Q}$	$\mathbb{R}\backslash\mathbb{Q}$	$\mathbb{R}$
$\sqrt{5}$					
8					Yes
-4					
$3\frac{1}{2}$					
$\frac{3\pi}{4}$					

(ii) In the case of $\sqrt{5}$, explain your choice in relation to the set of irrational numbers ($\mathbb{R}\backslash\mathbb{Q}$) (i.e. give a reason for writing either 'Yes' or 'No').

Solution

(i)

Number/Set	$\mathbb{N}$	$\mathbb{Z}$	$\mathbb{Q}$	$\mathbb{R}\backslash\mathbb{Q}$	$\mathbb{R}$
$\sqrt{5}$	No	No	No	Yes	Yes
8	Yes	Yes	Yes	No	Yes
-4	No	Yes	Yes	No	Yes
$3\frac{1}{2}$	No	No	Yes	No	Yes
$\frac{3\pi}{4}$	No	No	No	Yes	Yes

key point

8 is the only natural number, $\mathbb{N}$, in the question.

8 and -4 are the only integers, $\mathbb{Z}$.

8, -4 and $3\frac{1}{2}$ are all rational numbers, $\mathbb{Q}$.

$\sqrt{5}$ and $\frac{3\pi}{4}$ are both irrational numbers, while all the numbers are real, $\mathbb{R}$.

(ii) $\sqrt{5} = 2.236067977\ldots$ Since this decimal never repeats or terminates, it is a real number but cannot be written as a fraction.

exam focus

Both parts of this question were very badly answered by the vast majority of candidates. As a result, the total marks awarded was 5 marks with 3 marks for **any one** correct answer.

Remember, stick to your time budget and always write something in the space provided.

2 Algebraic Expressions

- ☐ To learn how to evaluate expressions.
- ☐ To learn how to simplify algebraic expressions.
- ☐ To learn how to add, subtract, multiply and divide algebraic fractions.

Evaluating expressions

To evaluate expressions given the value of the variables, substitute the values in for the variables and evaluate the expression.

Example
Find the value of $5(2p - q)$ when $p = -3$ and $q = 7$.

Solution
$5(2p - q)$
$= 5(2(-3) - (7))$ (let $p = -3$ and $q = 7$)
$= 5(-6 - 7)$
$= 5(-13)$
$= -65$

Take care when substituting in negative values. Always put brackets around these, then simplify the expression.

Example
Find the value of $a^2 - 6ab$ when $a = -2$ and $b = 3$.

Solution
$a^2 - 6ab$
$= (-2)^2 - 6(-2)(3)$ (let $a = -2$ and $b = 3$)
$= 4 - 6(-6)$ $((-2)^2 = (-2)(-2) = +4)$
$= 4 + 36$
$= 40$

Evaluating expressions is a vital skill for you to have throughout all aspects of your maths course.

Find the value of $\dfrac{2p - 1}{\sqrt{p^2 + 15}}$ when $p = -7$.

Solution

Replace each of the p's with the number -7: $\dfrac{2(-7) - 1}{\sqrt{(-7)^2 + 15}}$

$$= \dfrac{-14 - 1}{\sqrt{49 + 15}}$$

$$= \dfrac{-15}{\sqrt{64}}$$

$$= \dfrac{-15}{8}$$

Find the value of $\dfrac{5}{3x - 2} - \dfrac{7}{6x - 12}$, when $x = 4$.

Solution

$\dfrac{5}{3(4) - 2} - \dfrac{7}{6(4) - 12}$ (let $x = 4$)

$\dfrac{5}{12 - 2} - \dfrac{7}{24 - 12}$

$\dfrac{5}{10} - \dfrac{7}{12}$

$\dfrac{1}{2} - \dfrac{7}{12}$ (convert $\dfrac{1}{2}$ to $\dfrac{6}{12}$)

$\dfrac{6}{12} - \dfrac{7}{12}$

$-\dfrac{1}{12}$

Once you have substituted in the given values, you can use your calculator to simplify the calculations required.

Find the value of $\dfrac{2x - y + 3}{x^2 + 2y}$ when $x = \dfrac{3}{2}$ and $y = \dfrac{2}{3}$.

Solution

$\dfrac{2x - y + 3}{x^2 + 2y}$

$= \dfrac{2\left(\dfrac{3}{2}\right) - \left(\dfrac{2}{3}\right) + 3}{\left(\dfrac{3}{2}\right)^2 + 2\left(\dfrac{2}{3}\right)}$ $\qquad \left(\text{let } x = \dfrac{3}{2} \text{ and } y = \dfrac{2}{3}\right)$

$= \dfrac{3 - \dfrac{2}{3} + 3}{\dfrac{9}{4} + \dfrac{4}{3}}$

$= \dfrac{\dfrac{16}{3}}{\dfrac{43}{12}}$ $\qquad$ (add the fractions on the top and bottom)

$= \dfrac{16}{3} \times \dfrac{12}{43}$ $\qquad$ (turn the bottom fraction upside-down and multiply)

$= \dfrac{192}{129}$

$= \dfrac{64}{43}$ $\qquad$ (simplify by dividing 3 into the top and bottom)

Simplifying algebraic expressions

You must be able to apply the associative and distributive properties when simplifying algebraic expressions.

Associative property	Distributive property
$(A \times B) \times C = A \times (B \times C)$	$A(B + C) = AB + AC$
	$(A + B)(C + D) = A(C + D) + B(C + D)$

Example

Simplify $5(4x - 2) - 7(2x - 5)$.

Solution

$5(4x - 2) - 7(2x - 5)$ (remember $-7 \times -5 = 35$)

$= 20x - 10 - 14x + 35$ (multiply out the brackets)

$= 6x + 25$ (add like terms)

key point

Add and subtract like terms.

Example

Simplify $2a(4a + 3) - 4(3a - 7)$.

Solution

$2a(4a + 3) - 4(3a - 7)$

$= 8a^2 + 6a - 12a + 28$ (multiply out the brackets)

$= 8a^2 - 6a + 28$ (add like terms)

Express in its simplest form: $2x - [3 - (4 - 3x)] + 6$.

Solution

$2x - [3 - (4 - 3x)] + 6$

$= 2x - [3 - 4 + 3x] + 6$ (multiply out internal bracket)

$= 2x - [-1 + 3x] + 6$ (simplify)

$= 2x + 1 - 3x + 6$ (multiply out bracket)

$= -x + 7$ (simplify)

Example

Simplify $(2x + 3)(x - 4)$.

Solution

Key point: There are two methods for multiplying out brackets. These are both shown in this example. You can use whichever method you prefer.

Method 1: Use distributive law

$(2x + 3)(x - 4)$

$= 2x(x - 4) + 3(x - 4)$ (remember $+3 \times -4 = -12$)

$= 2x^2 - 8x + 3x - 12$ (multiply out the brackets)

$= 2x^2 - 5x - 12$ (add like terms)

Method 2: Use box method

Put the terms in the first bracket on the top and the terms from the second bracket down the side. Multiply each term by each other term.

	$2x$	$+3$
x	$2x^2$	$+3x$
-4	$-8x$	-12

Listing all terms from inside the boxes:

$2x^2 - 8x + 3x - 12$

$2x^2 - 5x - 12$ (add like terms)

Example

Simplify $(5a - 7)^2$.

Solution

$(5a - 7)^2 = (5a - 7)(5a - 7)$

Key point: A common mistake here is for candidates to just square the first term and square the second term, getting $25a^2 + 49$. This is incorrect. You **must** multiply out as shown.

	$5a$	-7
$5a$	$25a^2$	$-35a$
-7	$-35a$	$+49$

$25a^2 - 35a - 35a + 49$ (using box method)

$25a^2 - 70a + 49$ (add like terms)

Show that $(4x - 3)^2 + 24x$ is **positive** for all values of $x \in \mathbb{R}$.

Solution

$$(4x - 3)^2 + 24x$$

$$(4x-3)(4x-3)+24x$$

$$16x^2 - 12x - 12x + 9 + 24x$$

$$16x^2 + 9$$

Since, (any real number)$^2 \geq 0$, then $x^2 \geq 0$

Therefore, $16x^2 + 9 \geq 0$ and so $(4x - 3)^2 + 24x$ is positive for all values of $x \in \mathbb{R}$

Simplify $(3x - 4)(2x^2 + 5x - 2)$ and hence evaluate your answer when $x = -2$.

Solution

$(3x - 4)(2x^2 + 5x - 2)$

$= 3x(2x^2 + 5x - 2) - 4(2x^2 + 5x - 2)$

$= 6x^3 + 15x^2 - 6x - 8x^2 - 20x + 8$ (multiply out the brackets)

$= 6x^3 + 7x^2 - 26x + 8$ (add like terms)

Let $x = -2$:

$$6(-2)^3 + 7(-2)^2 - 26(-2) + 8$$

$$= 6(-8) + 7(4) + 52 + 8$$

$$= -48 + 28 + 60$$

$$= 40$$

The word 'hence' means that you **must** simplify the expression first and **then** let $x = -2$.

Multiplying and dividing algebraic fractions

Operations with algebraic fractions follow the same rules as in arithmetic. Before attempting to simplify when multiplying or dividing algebraic fractions, factorise where possible and divide the top and bottom by common factors. The contents of a bracket should be considered as a single term.

key point

When you multiply fractions, multiply top by top and bottom by bottom.

When you divide fractions, turn the second fraction upside-down and multiply.

Example

Simplify $\dfrac{8x^2}{5y^2} \times \dfrac{10y^2}{12x}$.

Solution

$\dfrac{8x^2}{5y^2} \times \dfrac{10y^2}{12x}$

$= \dfrac{80x^2y^2}{60xy^2}$ (multiply top by top and bottom by bottom)

$= \dfrac{80xxyy}{60xyy}$

$= \dfrac{4x}{3}$ (divide top and bottom by $20xyy$)

Example

Simplify $\dfrac{5a^2}{8b^2} \div \dfrac{5a}{16b^3}$.

Solution

$\dfrac{5a^2}{8b^2} \div \dfrac{5a}{16b^3}$

$= \dfrac{5a^2}{8b^2} \times \dfrac{16b^3}{5a}$

(Turn the second fraction upside-down and multiply. This means multiply by the reciprocal of $\dfrac{5a}{16b^3}$.)

$= \dfrac{80a^2b^3}{40ab^2}$

(multiply top by top and bottom by bottom)

$= \dfrac{80aabbb}{40abb}$

$= 2ab$

(divide top and bottom by $40abb$)

---

 exam Q

Simplify $\dfrac{x^2 - 2x}{6x + 9} \times \dfrac{4x + 6}{x - 2}$.

Solution

$\dfrac{x^2 - 2x}{6x + 9} \times \dfrac{4x + 6}{x - 2}$

$= \dfrac{x(x - 2)}{3(2x + 3)} \times \dfrac{2(2x + 3)}{x - 2}$

(factorise all parts)

$= \dfrac{2x(x - 2)(2x + 3)}{3(2x + 3)(x - 2)}$

(multiply top by top and bottom by bottom)

$= \dfrac{2x}{3}$

(divide top and bottom by $(x - 2)(2x + 3)$)

Simplify $\dfrac{x^2 + 8x + 15}{x^2 - 9} \div \dfrac{xy + 5y}{x^2 - 3x}$.

Solution

$$\dfrac{x^2 + 8x + 15}{x^2 - 9} \div \dfrac{xy + 5y}{x^2 - 3x}$$

$$= \dfrac{x^2 + 8x + 15}{x^2 - 9} \times \dfrac{x^2 - 3x}{xy + 5y}$$ (Turn the second fraction upside-down and multiply. This means to multiply by the reciprocal of $\dfrac{xy + 5y}{x^2 - 3x}$.)

$$= \dfrac{(x + 3)(x + 5)}{(x - 3)(x + 3)} \times \dfrac{x(x - 3)}{y(x + 5)}$$ (factorise all parts)

$$= \dfrac{x(x + 3)(x + 5)(x - 3)}{y(x - 3)(x + 3)(x + 5)}$$ (multiply top by top and bottom by bottom)

$$= \dfrac{x}{y}$$ (divide top and bottom by $(x + 3)(x + 5)(x - 3)$)

Adding and subtracting algebraic fractions

Algebraic fractions that have numbers as denominators can be added or subtracted in exactly the same way as in arithmetic, i.e. we express the fractions with the lowest common denominator (the LCM of the denominators).

Algebraic fractions are added or subtracted with the following steps:

1. Put brackets in where necessary.
2. Find the LCM of the expressions on the bottom.
3. Proceed in exactly the same way as in arithmetic.
4. Simplify the top (add and subtract terms which are the same).

Study the next example to understand the steps involved in adding and subtracting algebraic fractions.

Example

Simplify $\dfrac{x+3}{2} + \dfrac{2x-1}{5}$.

Solution

$$\dfrac{(x+3)}{2} + \dfrac{(2x-1)}{5}$$ (put brackets on top)

$$= \dfrac{?(x+3) + ?(2x-1)}{10}$$ (LCM of the denominators 2 and 5 is 10)

$$= \dfrac{5(x+3) + ?(2x-1)}{10}$$ (2 divides into 10, five times. Multiply 5 by the term on top of the 2.)

$$= \dfrac{5(x+3) + 2(2x-1)}{10}$$ (5 divides into 10, two times. Multiply 2 by the term on top of the 5.)

$$= \dfrac{5x + 15 + 4x - 2}{10}$$ (multiply out brackets)

$$= \dfrac{9x + 13}{10}$$ (simplify the top)

Simplify $\dfrac{x-4}{3} - \dfrac{3x-1}{6} + \dfrac{2x+5}{4}$.

Solution

$$\dfrac{(x-4)}{3} - \dfrac{(3x-1)}{6} + \dfrac{(2x+5)}{4}$$ (put brackets on top)

$$= \dfrac{?(x-4) - ?(3x-1) + ?(2x+5)}{12}$$

$$= \dfrac{4(x-4) - 2(3x-1) + 3(2x+5)}{12}$$ (LCM of the denominators 3, 6 and 4 is 12)

$$= \dfrac{4x - 16 - 6x + 2 + 6x + 15}{12}$$ (Multiply out brackets. Remember: $(-)(-) = +$)

$$= \dfrac{4x + 1}{12}$$ (simplify)

(i) Find the perimeter of the following parallelogram.

(ii) Express your answer as a single fraction.

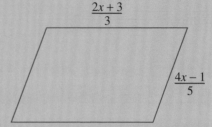

Solution

(i) Opposite sides of a parallelogram are equal in measure.

Perimeter = sum of all sides

$$\text{Perimeter} = 2\left(\frac{2x + 3}{3}\right) + 2\left(\frac{4x - 1}{5}\right)$$

(ii) $\text{Perimeter} = \dfrac{2(2x + 3)}{3} + \dfrac{2(4x - 1)}{5}$

$$= \frac{?[2(2x + 3)] + ?[2(4x - 1)]}{15}$$

$$= \frac{5[2(2x + 3)] + 3[2(4x - 1)]}{15}$$

$$= \frac{10(2x + 3) + 6(4x - 1)}{15}$$

$$= \frac{20x + 30 + 24x - 6}{15}$$

$$= \frac{44x + 24}{15}$$

Fractions which have unknowns in the denominator

Algebraic fractions that have unknowns in the denominators can be added or subtracted in exactly the same way as in arithmetic, i.e. we express the fractions with the lowest common denominator (the LCM of the denominators).

Algebraic fractions are added or subtracted with the same steps as before.

Write the following as a single fraction.

$$\frac{5}{2x + 1} - \frac{x}{4}$$

Solution

Multiply each fraction by a suitable term or terms, to make them have the same denominator.

LCM of the denominators of $(2x + 1)$ and 4 is $(2x + 1)(4)$

$$\frac{4}{4} \times \frac{5}{2x + 1} - \frac{x}{4} \times \frac{(2x + 1)}{(2x + 1)}$$ (multiply the first fraction top and bottom by 4
multiply the second fraction top and bottom by $(2x + 1)$)

$$\frac{(4)(5)}{4(2x + 1)} - \frac{x(2x + 1)}{4(2x + 1)}$$

$$\frac{20}{8x + 4} - \frac{2x^2 + x}{8x + 4}$$ (multiply out the brackets)

$$\frac{20 - (2x^2 + x)}{8x + 4}$$ (bring the fractions together)

$$\frac{20 - 2x^2 - x}{8x + 4}$$ (simplify)

Simplify $\dfrac{2}{x - 3} - \dfrac{7}{2x + 5} + \dfrac{2}{3}$.

Solution

LCM of the denominators of $(x - 3)$, $(2x + 5)$ and 3 is $(x - 3)(2x + 5)(3)$:

$$\frac{?(2) - ?(7) + ?(2)}{(x - 3)(2x + 5)(3)}$$ (LCM is $(x - 3)(2x + 5)(3)$)

$$= \frac{2(2x + 5)(3) - 7(x - 3)(3) + 2(x - 3)(2x + 5)}{(x - 3)(2x + 5)(3)}$$

$$= \frac{2(6x + 15) - 7(3x - 9) + 2(2x^2 + 5x - 6x - 15)}{(x - 3)(2x + 5)(3)}$$ (multiply out brackets)

$$= \frac{12x + 30 - 21x + 63 + 2(2x^2 - 1x - 15)}{(x - 3)(2x + 5)(3)}$$ (multiply out brackets)

$$= \frac{-9x + 93 + 4x^2 - 2x - 30}{(x - 3)(2x + 5)(3)}$$ (multiply out brackets)

$$= \frac{4x^2 - 11x + 63}{(x - 3)(2x + 5)(3)}$$ (simplify)

3 Factorising

☐ To learn how to factorise algebraic expressions.
☐ To become familiar with the four different types of factorising.

Factorising and simplifying expressions

There are four types of factorising that we will meet on this course:

Take out common terms	Factorising by grouping
$ab + ad = a(b + d)$	$ab + ad + cb + cd = (a + c)(b + d)$
Factorise a trinomial (3 terms)	**Difference of two squares**
$a^2 - 2ab + b^2 = (a - b)(a - b)$	$a^2 - b^2 = (a + b)(a - b)$

exam
focus

Factorising is a basic and vital skill for you to have throughout your maths course. You must be able to factorise expressions quickly and easily. This will take practice, but it is worthwhile spending time on.

Factorising is the reverse process of expanding brackets. You could use the box method to verify your factors.

$$
\begin{array}{c|c|c}
 & a & b \\
\hline
a & a^2 & ab \\
\hline
-b & -ab & -b^2 \\
\end{array}
\qquad
\begin{aligned}
&= a^2 + ab - ab - b^2 \\
&= a^2 - b^2
\end{aligned}
$$

1. Take out common terms

1. Find the highest common factor (HCF) of all the terms making up the expression. This is the biggest value (constants or variables) that divides into all terms evenly.
2. Put the HCF outside the brackets.
3. Divide each term by the HCF to find the factor inside the brackets.

Example

Factorise the following:

(i) $3p^2 + 6pq$

(ii) $ab - 2a^2b + 3ab^2$

Solution

(i) $3p^2 + 6pq$

$\quad = 3pp + 6pq \quad$ (HCF is $3p$)

$\quad = 3p(p + 2q) \quad$ (factorise out $3p$)

(ii) $ab - 2a^2b + 3ab^2$

$\quad = ab - 2aab + 3abb \quad$ (HCF is ab)

$\quad = ab(1 - 2a + 3b) \quad$ (factorise out ab)

Factorise the following:

(i) $20xy - 4x^2$

(ii) $6a^3 + 24ab$

Solution

(i) $20xy - 4x^2$

$\quad = 20xy - 4xx \quad$ (HCF is $4x$)

$\quad = 4x(5y - x) \quad$ (factorise out $4x$)

(ii) $6a^3 + 24ab$

$\quad = 6aaa + 24ab \quad$ (HCF is $6a$)

$\quad = 6a(a^2 + 4b) \quad$ (factorise out $6a$)

2. Factorise by grouping

Use this method when you have four terms, with no common factor.

1. Group into pairs with a common factor.
2. Take out the HCF in each pair separately.
3. Take out the new common factor.

Example

Factorise the following:

(i) $3pr - 3ps + qr - qs$ (ii) $a^2 + xy - ay - ax$

Solution

(i) $3pr - 3ps + qr - qs$ (already in pairs with a common factor)

    $= 3p(r - s) + q(r - s)$ (take out common factor in each pair)

    $= (r - s)(3p + q)$ (take out the common factor $(r - s)$)

(ii) $a^2 + xy - ay - ax$ (No common factors in the first pair. Need to rearrange.)

    $= a^2 - ay + xy - ax$ (rearrange order of the terms so that they are grouped into pairs with a common factor)

    $= a(a - y) - x(-y + a)$ (take out common factor in each pair)

    $= a(a - y) - x(a - y)$

    $= (a - y)(a - x)$ (take out the common factor $(a - y)$)

Example

Factorise the following:

(i) $ab - cb + ac - c^2$ (ii) $3p - c + 3pc - c^2$

Solution

(i) $ab - cb + ac - c^2$ (already in pairs with a common factor)

    $= b(a - c) + c(a - c)$ (take out common factor in each pair)

    $= (a - c)(b + c)$ (take out the common factor $(a - c)$)

(ii) $3p - c + 3pc - c^2$ (already in pairs with a common factor)

    $= 1(3p - c) + c(3p - c)$ (take out common factor in each pair)

    $= (3p - c)(1 + c)$ (take out the common factor $(3p - c)$)

Factorise the following:

(i) $5fh - 2h^2 - 6h + 15f$ **(ii)** $4c^2 - 3d - 2cd + 6c$

Solution

(i) $5fh - 2h^2 - 6h + 15f$ (already in pairs with a common factor, but will be easier if we

    $= 5fh - 2h^2 + 15f - 6h$ rearrange to have the *f* in the first position in each pair.)

    $= h(5f - 2h) + 3(5f - 2h)$ (take out the common factors in each pair)

    $= (5f - 2h)(h + 3)$ (take out the common factor $(5f - 2h)$

(ii) $4c^2 - 3d - 2cd + 6c$ (No common factors in the first pair.

                                  Need to rearrange.)

    $= 4c^2 - 2cd + 6c - 3d$ (rearrange order of the terms so that they are grouped

                                    into pairs with a common factor)

    $= 2c(2c - d) + 3(2c - d)$ (take out common factor in each pair)

    $= (2c - d)(2c + 3)$ (take out the common factor $(2c - d)$)

3. Quadratic trinomials

An expression in the form $ax^2 + bx + c$, where a, b and c are numbers, is called a quadratic trinomial. This is because in the expression the highest power of x is 2 (quadratic) and it contains three terms (trinomial).

For factorising, quadratic trinomials can be broken into two types:

1. **Final term is positive**

   When the final term is positive, the signs inside the middle of the brackets will be the **same**: either both plus or both minus. Keep the sign of the middle term given in the question.

2. **Final term is negative**

   When the final term is negative, the signs inside the middle of the brackets will be **different**.

Use trial and improvement to find the factors. Multiply the inside terms, multiply the outside terms and add the results to see if you get the middle term of the original quadratic trinomial.

Example

Factorise $x^2 - 7x + 10$.

Solution

$x^2 - 7x + 10$ (final term, $+10$, is positive, so the signs in the brackets are the same)

$= (x - 2)(x - 5)$

Check: outside terms $= (x)(-5) = -5x$

   inside terms $= (-2)(x) = \underline{-2x}$

     sum $=$ $-7x =$ middle term of original quadratic trinomial

Therefore, factors $(x - 2)(x - 5)$ are correct.

Check your answers:

	x	-2
x	x^2	$-2x$
-5	$-5x$	10

$= x^2 - 2x - 5x + 10$
$= x^2 - 7x + 10$

Alternative method:

$1x^2 - 7x + 10$ $1 \times 10 = 10$ ($+10$ is the guide number – it tells you that
M A M   both signs are the same)

We need factors of 10 which add to give -7.

$M = 10$	$A = -7$
$1 \times 10 = 10$	$1 + 10 = 11$
$2 \times 5 = 10$	$2 + 5 = 7$
$-2 \times -5 = 10$	$-2 - 5 = -7$

The factors which fit this criteria are -2 and -5.

Rewrite the trinomial, replacing $-7x$ with $-2x$ and $-5x$.

$1x^2 - 2x - 5x + 10$

$x(x - 2) - 5(x - 2)$ (factorise by grouping)

$(x - 2)(x - 5)$

Example

Factorise $2x^2 - 9x - 5$.

Solution

$2x^2 - 9x - 5$ (final term, -5, is negative, so the signs in the brackets are different)

$= (2x + 1)(x - 5)$

Check: outside terms $= (2x)(-5) = -10x$

          inside terms $= (1)(x)$ $= \underline{\quad x \quad}$

                sum $=$ $-9x =$ middle term of original quadratic trinomial

Therefore, factors $(2x + 1)(x - 5)$ are correct.

Check your answers:

	$2x$	$+1$
x	$2x^2$	x
-5	$-10x$	-5

$= 2x^2 + x - 10x - 5$
$= 2x^2 - 9x - 5$

Alternative method:

$2x^2 - 9x - 5$ $2 \times -5 = -10$ (-10 is the guide number – it tells you that
M   A   M   both signs are different)

We need factors of -10 which add to give -9.

$M = -10$	$A = -9$
$-1 \times 10 = -10$	$-1 + 10 = 9$
$1 \times -10 = -10$	$1 - 10 = -9$
$-2 \times 5 = -10$	$-2 + 5 = 3$
$2 \times -5 = -10$	$2 - 5 = -3$

The factors which fit the criteria of the guide number are 1 and -10.

Rewrite the trinomial, replacing $-9x$ with $1x$ and $-10x$.

$2x^2 + 1x - 10x - 5$

$x(2x + 1) - 5(2x + 1)$ (factorise by grouping)

$(2x + 1)(x - 5)$

Example

Factorise $8x^2 + 2x - 15$.

Solution

$8x^2 + 2x - 15$ (final term, -15, is negative, so the signs in the brackets are different)

$= (4x - 5)(2x + 3)$

Check: outside terms $= (4x)(3)$ $=$ $12x$

         inside terms $= (-5)(2x) = \underline{-10x}$

             sum $=$ $2x =$ middle term of original quadratic trinomial

Therefore, factors $(4x - 5)(2x + 3)$ are correct.

> **key point**
>
> This question involves a lot of trial and improvement. You need to eliminate possibilities such as $(8x + ?)(x + ?)$, etc.

Alternative method:

$8x^2 + 2x - 15$ $8 \times -15 = -120$ (this is the guide number – it tells you that
M   A   M   both signs are different)

We need factors of -120 which add to give $+2$.

$$
\begin{array}{c|c}
M = -120 & A = +2 \\
\hline
-10 \times 12 = -120 & -10 + 12 = +2
\end{array}
$$

The factors which fit this criteria are -10 and 12.

Rewrite the trinomial, replacing $+2x$ with $-10x$ and $12x$.

$8x^2 - 10x + 12x - 15$

$2x(4x - 5) + 3(4x - 5)$ (factorise by grouping)

$(4x - 5)(2x + 3)$

exam focus

Some quadratic trinomials can be very challenging to factorise. Do not be discouraged! If you cannot find the correct factors straight away, keep going until you have tried all options.

4. Difference of two squares

An expression such as $a^2 - b^2$ is called the 'difference of two squares'.

> 1. Write each term as a perfect square with brackets.
> 2. Use the rule $a^2 - b^2 = (a - b)(a + b)$.

key point

> The difference of two squares is a special case of a trinomial. $x^2 - 25$ can be written as $x^2 + 0x - 25$ and factorised as $(x + 5)(x - 5)$.

Example

Factorise the following:

(i) $x^2 - 16$

(ii) $4x^2 - 49$

Solution

(i) $x^2 - 16$

$\quad = x^2 - (4)^2$

$\quad = (x + 4)(x - 4)$

(ii) $4x^2 - 49$

$\quad = (2x)^2 - (7)^2$

$\quad = (2x + 7)(2x - 7)$

Example

Factorise the following:

(i) $25p^2 - 64q^2$

(ii) $3x^2 - 12y^2$

Solution

(i) $25p^2 - 64q^2$

$\quad = (5p)^2 - (8q)^2$

$\quad = (5p + 8q)(5p - 8q)$

(ii) $3x^2 - 12y^2$

$\quad = 3(x^2 - 4y^2) \qquad$ (take out common factor)

$\quad = 3(x^2 - (2y)^2)$

$\quad = 3(x + 2y)(x - 2y)$

Preparing for the exam

You must practise the previous four different types of factorising and be able to recognise when to use each type. In the exam you may be given a number of expressions to factorise. It is up to you to know which method of factorising to use.

Example

Factorise fully each of the following:

(i) $20xy - 4x^2$ (ii) $5x^2 - 9x - 2$

Solution

(i) Take out common factors:

$$20xy - 4x^2$$

$$= 4x(5y - x)$$

(ii) Quadratic trinomial:

$$5x^2 - 9x - 2$$

$$= (5x + 1)(x - 2)$$

Factorise fully each of the following expressions:

(i) $5x^3 - 10x^2$

(ii) $4x^2 - 81y^2$

(iii) $a^2 - ab + 3a - 3b$

Solution

(i) To factorise $5x^3 - 10x^2$, you must take out common factors:

$5x^3 - 10x^2$ (HCF is $5x^2$)

$= 5x^2(x - 2)$ (factorise out $5x^2$)

(ii) To factorise $4x^2 - 81y^2$, you must find the difference of two squares:

$4x^2 - 81y^2$

$= (2x)^2 - (9y)^2$

$= (2x + 9y)(2x - 9y)$

(iii) To factorise $a^2 - ab + 3a - 3b$, you must factorise by grouping:

$a^2 - ab + 3a - 3b$

$= a(a - b) + 3(a - b)$

$= (a - b)(a + 3)$

As shown here, you may be asked to use different types of factorising in the one exam question. You must be able to recognise which type of factorising is needed in each case. For this question, each part was worth 5 marks.

Factorise fully each of the following expressions:

(i) $9x^2 - 64y^2$

(ii) $3xy - 10x - 10b + 3by$

(iii) $6x^2 - 7x - 24$

Solution

(i) To factorise $9x^2 - 64y^2$, you must find the difference of two squares:

$9x^2 - 64y^2$

$= (3x)^2 - (8y)^2$

$= (3x + 8y)(3x - 8y)$

(ii) To factorise $3xy - 10x - 10b + 3by$, you must factorise by grouping:

$3xy - 10x - 10b + 3by$

$= 3xy + 3by - 10x - 10b$ (rearrange)

$= 3y(x + b) - 10(x + b)$ (factorise)

$= (3y - 10)(x + b)$

Rearranging was not essential but it made the question easier.

(iii) To factorise $6x^2 - 7x - 24$, you must factorise a quadratic trinomial:

$6x^2 - 7x - 24$

$= (3x - 8)(2x + 3)$

This is a very challenging trinomial to factorise. Use trial and improvement to find the correct factors.

(i) Factorise $8x^2 - 12x$.

(ii) Factorise $4x^2 - 12x + 9$.

(iii) Simplify $\dfrac{8x^2 - 12x}{4x^2 - 12x + 9}$.

Solution

(i) $8x^2 - 12x$ (HCF is $4x$)

    $= 4x(2x - 3)$ (factorise out $4x$)

(ii) $4x^2 - 12x + 9$

    $= (2x - 3)(2x - 3)$

(iii) $\dfrac{8x^2 - 12x}{4x^2 - 12x + 9}$

    $= \dfrac{4x(2x - 3)}{(2x - 3)(2x - 3)}$

    $= \dfrac{4x}{(2x - 3)}$

This question was worth 20 marks, awarded as follows:
Part (i) = 5 marks, (ii) = 10 marks and (iii) = 5 marks.

Simplify $\dfrac{x^2 + 7x + 12}{x^2 + 2x - 3}$.

Solution

$= \dfrac{(x + 3)(x + 4)}{(x + 3)(x - 1)}$ (factorise the top and bottom)

$= \dfrac{x + 4}{x - 1}$ (divide top and bottom by $(x + 3)$)

One of the factors of $8x^2 + 45x - 18$ is $x + 6$.

(i) Factorise $8x^2 + 45x - 18$

(ii) Write down one quadratic expression in x, other than $8x^2 + 45x - 18$, that has $x + 6$ as a factor.

Give your answer in the form $ax^2 + bx + c$, where $a, b, c \in \mathbb{R}$.

Solution

(i) $8x^2 + 45x - 18 = (x + 6)(\ ?\ )$ (Factorise using any appropriate method)

                $= (x + 6)(8x - 3)$

(ii) $(x + 6)(\ ?\ )$

    $(x + 6)(2x + 1)$ (put any linear expression in the form $(px + q)$ into the second bracket)

    $2x^2 + 1x + 12x + 6$ (multiply out)

    $2x^2 + 13x + 6$

Simplify $(7x - 2)(7x + 2) - (5y - 2)(5y + 2)$ and fully factorise the simplified expression.

Solution

Simplify: $(7x - 2)(7x + 2) - (5y - 2)(5y + 2)$

           $= (49x^2 + 14x - 14x - 4) - (25y^2 + 10y - 10y - 4)$

           $= (49x^2 - 4) - (25y^2 - 4)$

           $= 49x^2 - 4 - 25y^2 + 4$

           $= 49x^2 - 25y^2$

Now factorise $49x^2 - 25y^2$ using the difference of two squares:

           $= (7x)^2 - (5y)^2$

           $= (7x + 5y)(7x - 5y)$

4 Changing the Subject of a Formula

□ To learn how to rearrange expressions, to change the subject of a formula.

□ To know how to manipulate a formula in an in-context question.

When we rearrange a formula so that one of the variables is given in terms of the others, we are said to be **changing the subject of the formula or manipulating the formulae**. We do this to express one variable in terms of the other variables. The rules in changing the subject of a formula are the same as when solving an equation. That is, we can:

1. **Add** or **subtract** the same quantity to both sides.
2. **Multiply** or **divide** both sides by the same quantity.
3. **Square** both sides, **cube** both sides, etc.
4. Take the **square root** of both sides, take the **cube root** of both sides, etc.

Whatever letter comes after the word 'express' is to be on its own. In the case of equations given in words, the variable we are looking for must be the one on its own.

Three common errors made when manipulating formulae are:

1. $\dfrac{1}{a} + \dfrac{1}{b} \neq \dfrac{1}{a+b}$ 2. $\dfrac{a}{b+c} \neq \dfrac{a}{b} + \dfrac{a}{c}$ 3. $a\left(\dfrac{b}{c}\right) \neq \dfrac{ab}{ac}$

These are common errors that candidates make when working with fractions. You should revise fractions to fully understand what is wrong with each of these errors.

Changing the subject of a formula (manipulating a formula) is an essential skill, which arises in many sections of the course. These include Area and Volume, Trigonometry and Coordinate Geometry.

Example

Rearrange the equation $ab + cd = e$ to make a the subject of the formula.

Solution

$$ab + cd = e$$

$$ab + cd - cd = e - cd \qquad \text{(subtract } cd \text{ from both sides)}$$

$$ab = e - cd$$

$$\frac{ab}{b} = \frac{e - cd}{b} \qquad \text{(divide both sides by } b\text{)}$$

$$a = \frac{e - cd}{b}$$

Temperature can be measured in degrees Celsius or degrees Fahrenheit. The formula for converting from one to the other is given by $C = \frac{5}{9}(F - 32°)$.

  (i) Rearrange this formula to find F in terms of C.

  (ii) Hence, convert 25°C into degrees Fahrenheit.

Solution

(i)
$$C = \frac{5}{9}(F - 32°)$$

$$9(C) = 9\left(\frac{5}{9}(F - 32°)\right) \qquad \text{(multiply both sides by 9)}$$

$$9C = 5(F - 32°)$$

$$9C = 5F - 160° \qquad \text{(multiply out the bracket)}$$

$$9C + 160° = 5F - 160° + 160° \qquad \text{(add 160° to both sides)}$$

$$9C + 160° = 5F$$

$$\frac{9C + 160°}{5} = F \qquad \text{(divide both sides by 5)}$$

(ii) $F = \dfrac{9(25°) + 160°}{5} \qquad \text{(let C = 25°)}$

$$F = \frac{225° + 160°}{5} = \frac{385°}{5} = 77° \qquad \text{(therefore, 25°C = 77°F)}$$

Example

Given that $z = \sqrt{y - x}$, write x in terms of z and y.

Solution

$$z = \sqrt{y - x}$$

$$(z)^2 = (\sqrt{y - x})^2 \quad \text{(square both sides)}$$

$$z^2 = y - x$$

$$z^2 + x = y - x + x \quad \text{(add } x \text{ to both sides)}$$

$$z^2 + x = y$$

$$z^2 + x - z^2 = y - z^2 \quad \text{(subtract } z^2 \text{ from both sides)}$$

$$x = y - z^2$$

Example

Given that $2(2q - 7p) = q(3p - q)$, express p in terms of q.

Solution

$$2(2q - 7p) = q(3p - q)$$

$$4q - 14p = 3pq - q^2 \quad \text{(multiply out brackets)}$$

$$4q - 14p + 14p = 3pq - q^2 + 14p \quad \text{(add } 14p \text{ to both sides)}$$

$$4q = 3pq - q^2 + 14p \quad \text{(simplify)}$$

$$4q + q^2 = 3pq - q^2 + 14p + q^2 \quad \text{(add } q^2 \text{ to both sides)}$$

$$4q + q^2 = 3pq + 14p \quad \text{(simplify)}$$

$$4q + q^2 = p(3q + 14) \quad \text{(factorise out } p\text{)}$$

$$\frac{4q + q^2}{3q + 14} = \frac{p(3q + 14)}{3q + 14} \quad \text{(divide both sides by } 3q + 14\text{)}$$

$$\frac{4q + q^2}{3q + 14} = p$$

A capacitor is a device which stores electricity. The formula $W = \frac{1}{2}C V^2$ gives the energy stored in the capacitor, where W is the energy, C is the capacitance and V is the voltage, and standard units are used throughout.

(i) Find the amount of energy stored in a capacitor when $C = 2\ 500$ and $V = 32$.

(ii) Write V in terms of W and C.

Solution

(i) $W = \dfrac{1}{2}C V^2$

$W = \dfrac{1}{2}(2\ 500)(32)^2$ (let $C = 2\ 500$ and $V = 32$)

$W = 1\ 280\ 000$

(ii) $W = \dfrac{1}{2}C V^2$

$2(W) = 2\left(\dfrac{1}{2}C V^2\right)$ (multiply both sides by 2)

$2W = C V^2$ (simplify)

$\dfrac{2W}{C} = \dfrac{C V^2}{C}$ (divide both sides by C)

$\dfrac{2W}{C} = V^2$ (simplify)

$\sqrt{\dfrac{2W}{C}} = V$ (square root both sides)

The 'multiplier' is a variable used by economists to measure the effect of an increase in spending in the economy.

One version of the multiplier is $M = \frac{1}{S+P}$, where M is the multiplier, S relates to savings and P relates to imports.

(i) Calculate the value of M, the multiplier, if $S = 0.2$ and $P = 0.1$.

(ii) Explain the effect on the size of M if the value of P increases.

(iii) Sometimes the above formula is used to calculate P. Rearrange the formula to make P its subject.

Solution

(i) $M = \dfrac{1}{S+P}$

$M = \dfrac{1}{0.2 + 0.1}$ (let $S = 0.2$ and $P = 0.1$)

$M = \dfrac{1}{0.3}$

$M = \dfrac{10}{3}$

(ii) As the size of P increases, the denominator on the right-hand side increases and so the overall value of the fraction decreases. Therefore, as P increases, M decreases.

(iii) $M = \dfrac{1}{S+P}$

$(S+P)M = (S+P)\left(\dfrac{1}{S+P}\right)$ (multiply both sides by $(S+P)$)

$SM + PM = 1$

$SM + PM - SM = 1 - SM$ (subtract SM from both sides)

$PM = 1 - SM$

$P = \dfrac{1 - SM}{M}$ (divide both sides by M)

(i) In the study of optical lenses, there is a relationship between the focal length, f, of the lens, the distance the object is placed from the lens, u, and the distance the image is formed from the lens, v. This relationship is expressed as follows: $\dfrac{1}{f} = \dfrac{1}{u} + \dfrac{1}{v}$. Manipulate this formula to express v in terms of the other variables.

(ii) An object is placed a distance of 20 cm from a lens with a focal length of 15 cm. Find the distance the image is formed from the lens.

Solution

(i)
$$\frac{1}{f} = \frac{1}{u} + \frac{1}{v}$$

$$fuv\left(\frac{1}{f}\right) = fuv\left(\frac{1}{u}\right) + fuv\left(\frac{1}{v}\right) \qquad \text{(multiply all parts by the LCM } fuv\text{)}$$

$$uv = fv + fu$$

$$uv - fv = fv + fu - fv \qquad \text{(subtract } fv \text{ from both sides)}$$

$$uv - fv = fu$$

$$v(u - f) = fu \qquad \text{(factorise out } v\text{)}$$

$$\frac{v(u - f)}{(u - f)} = \frac{fu}{(u - f)} \qquad \text{(divide both sides by } (u - f)\text{)}$$

$$v = \frac{fu}{u - f}$$

(ii) $f = 15$ and $u = 20$:
$$v = \frac{fu}{u - f}$$

$$v = \frac{(15)(20)}{20 - 15}$$

$$v = \frac{300}{5}$$

$$v = 60$$

Therefore, the image is formed 60 cm from the lens.

5 Solving Linear Equations

aims

☐ To learn how to solve linear equations.
☐ To learn how to form and solve linear equations in in-context questions.

An equation is solved with the following method:

Whatever you do to one side, you must do exactly the same to the other side.

key point

Keep balance in mind. The solution of an equation is the number that makes both sides balance. You can test if an answer is a solution by substituting it into the original equation and checking that the equation balances (i.e. left side = right side).

Example

Solve $2x - 7 = 23$.

Solution

$$2x - 7 = 23$$
$$2x - 7 + 7 = 23 + 7 \quad \text{(add 7 to both sides to remove the } -7 \text{ from the left-hand side)}$$
$$2x = 30 \quad \text{(simplify)}$$
$$\frac{2x}{2} = \frac{30}{2} \quad \text{(divide both sides by 2 to remove the 2 from the LHS)}$$
$$x = 15$$

Example

Solve $3(x - 2) + 1 = 19$.

Solution

$$3(x - 2) + 1 = 19$$

$3x - 6 + 1 = 19$ (multiply out brackets)

$3x - 5 = 19$ (simplify)

$3x - 5 + 5 = 19 + 5$ (add 5 to both sides)

$3x = 24$ (simplify)

$x = 8$ (divide both sides by 3)

Example

Given that $3a(x + 5) = 114$, find the value of x when $a = 4$.

Solution

$$3a(x + 5) = 114$$

$3(4)(x + 5) = 114$ (let $a = 4$)

$12(x + 5) = 114$

$12x + 60 = 114$ (simplify)

$12x = 114 - 60$ (subtract 60 from both sides)

$12x = 54$

$x = 4{\cdot}5$ (divide both sides by 12)

(i) Given that $x = 2t - 1$ and $y = \frac{2}{3}t + 2$, express $3x - y + 2$ in terms of t, in its simplest form.

(ii) Hence, find the value of t when $3x - y + 2 = 0$.

Solution

(i) $3x - y + 2$ Let $x = 2t - 1$ and $y = \frac{2}{3}t + 2$

$$3(2t - 1) - \left(\frac{2}{3}t + 2\right) + 2$$

$6t - 3 - \dfrac{2}{3}t - 2 + 2$

$6t - 3 - \dfrac{2}{3}t$

$6t - \dfrac{2}{3}t - 3$

$\dfrac{16}{3}t - 3$

Part (i) of this question is purely substitution. There is no equal sign, so it is not an equation. Therefore, we cannot multiply all parts by 3.

(ii) $3x - y + 2 = 0$

$\dfrac{16}{3}t - 3 = 0$ $(3x - y + 2 = \dfrac{16}{3}t - 3$ from part (i))

$\dfrac{16}{3}t = 3$ $(\times 3)$

$16t = 9$ $(\div 16)$

$t = \dfrac{9}{16}$

A plumber charges €90 for a service call plus €1·25 for each additional minute of service over 60 minutes. If the bill for a plumbing repair job was €125, how many minutes did the service call take?

Solution

Let n = number of minutes of the call.
Then $(n - 60)$ is the number of additional minutes, after the first 60 minutes of the service call.

Form an equation:

service charge + €1·25 per additional minute = cost of the service call

$90 + 1 \cdot 25(n - 60) = 125$

$90 + 1 \cdot 25n - 75 = 125$ (simplify)

$15 + 1 \cdot 25n = 125$

$1 \cdot 25n = 110$ (subtract 5 from both sides)

$n = 88$ (divide both sides by 1·25)

Therefore, the plumber spent 88 minutes doing the service call.

A goldsmith combined pure gold that costs €5·20 per gram with 50 g of a gold alloy that costs €2·80 per gram. How many grams of the pure gold were used to make an alloy of gold that costs €4·40 a gram?

Solution

Let x = number of grams of pure gold.

Form an equation.

$$\begin{bmatrix} €5·20(\text{grams of pure gold}) \\ + \\ €2·80(\text{grams of gold alloy}) \end{bmatrix} = €4·40(\text{total grams of pure gold + gold alloy})$$

$$€5·20(x) + €2·80(50) = €4·40(x + 50)$$

$$€5·20(x) + €140 = €4·40(x) + €220$$

$$€5·20(x) - €4·40(x) = €220 - €140$$

$$€0·80(x) = €80$$

$$x = 100$$

Therefore, 100 g of pure gold was added.

Equations with fractions

If there are fractions **in an equation**, multiply all parts by a number that all of the denominators divide evenly into. This number is known as the lowest common multiple (LCM) of the denominators.

Example

Solve the equation $\frac{1}{2}(7x - 2) + 5 = 2x + 7$.

Solution

$$\frac{1}{2}(7x - 2) + 5 = 2x + 7$$

$$2\left(\frac{1}{2}(7x - 2)\right) + 2(5) = 2(2x) + 2(7) \quad \text{(multiply each term by 2)}$$

$$1(7x - 2) + 2(5) = 2(2x) + 2(7) \quad \text{(divide the denominators into the LCM)}$$

$$7x - 2 + 10 = 4x + 14 \quad \text{(multiply out brackets)}$$

$$7x + 8 = 4x + 14 \quad \text{(simplify)}$$

$$7x - 4x = 14 - 8 \quad \text{(rearrange)}$$

$$3x = 6 \quad \text{(simplify)}$$

$$x = 2 \quad \text{(divide both sides by 3)}$$

Example

Solve the equation $\dfrac{x - 7}{2} = \dfrac{x + 3}{6}$.

Solution

$$\frac{x - 7}{2} = \frac{x + 3}{6}$$

$$6\left(\frac{x - 7}{2}\right) = 6\left(\frac{x + 3}{6}\right) \qquad \text{(multiply each term by 6)}$$

$$3(x - 7) = 1(x + 3) \qquad \text{(divide the denominators into the LCM)}$$

$$3x - 21 = x + 3 \qquad \text{(multiply out brackets)}$$

$$3x - x = 3 + 21 \qquad \text{(rearrange)}$$

$$2x = 24 \qquad \text{(simplify)}$$

$$x = 12 \qquad \text{(divide both sides by 2)}$$

Solve the equation $\dfrac{3(x + 3)}{4} - \dfrac{2(x - 3)}{3} = \dfrac{x + 1}{2}$.

Solution

$$\frac{3(x + 3)}{4} - \frac{2(x - 3)}{3} = \frac{x + 1}{2} \qquad \text{(the LCM of 4, 3 and 2 is 12)}$$

$$12\left(\frac{3(x + 3)}{4}\right) - 12\left(\frac{2(x - 3)}{3}\right) = 12\left(\frac{x + 1}{2}\right) \qquad \text{(multiply each term by 12)}$$

$$3(3(x + 3)) - 4(2(x - 3)) = 6(x + 1) \qquad \text{(divide the denominators into the LCM)}$$

$$9(x + 3) - 8(x - 3) = 6(x + 1)$$

$$9x + 27 - 8x + 24 = 6x + 6 \qquad \text{(multiply out brackets)}$$

$$x + 51 = 6x + 6 \qquad \text{(simplify)}$$

$$51 - 6 = 6x - x \qquad \text{(rearrange)}$$

$$45 = 5x \qquad \text{(divide both sides by 5)}$$

$$9 = x$$

(i) x represents an even number. Explain why $x + 2$ is the next even number.

(ii) If one-third of the smaller even number is subtracted from half of the larger even number, the result is 8. Find the value of x.

Solution

(i) 2 is the lowest even number, so adding 2 onto an even number will give the next even number.

(ii) When one-third of the smaller even number is subtracted from half of the larger even number, the result is 8.

$$\frac{1}{2}\text{(larger number)} - \frac{1}{3}\text{(smaller number)} = 8$$

$$\frac{1}{2}(x + 2) - \frac{1}{3}(x) = 8 \qquad (\times\,6)$$

$$6\left[\frac{1}{2}(x + 2)\right] - 6\left[\frac{1}{3}(x)\right] = 6(8)$$

$$3(x + 2) - 2(x) = 48$$

$$3x + 6 - 2x = 48$$

$$3x - 2x = 48 - 6$$

$$x = 42$$

Take care with the phrase 'is subtracted from'.

The first thing mentioned comes second in the mathematical expression.

For example: 5 is subtracted from 3 means: $3 - 5$

x is subtracted from y means: $y - x$

The three angles of a triangle are:

$$\frac{8(x-2)}{3}, \; 4x+7, \; \frac{5x-10}{2}.$$

Find the value of x.

Solution

The three angles of a triangle sum to 180°.

$$\left(\frac{8(x-2)}{3}\right) + (4x+7) + \left(\frac{5x-10}{2}\right) = 180$$

$$6\left(\frac{8(x-2)}{3}\right) + 6(4x+7) + 6\left(\frac{5x-10}{2}\right) = 6(180) \quad \text{(multiply each term by 6)}$$

$$2(8(x-2)) + 6(4x+7) + 3(5x-10) = 6(180) \quad \text{(divide the denominators into the LCM)}$$

$$16(x-2) + 24x + 42 + 15x - 30 = 1\,080 \quad \text{(multiply out brackets)}$$

$$16x - 32 + 39x + 12 = 1\,080 \quad \text{(simplify)}$$

$$55x - 20 = 1\,080$$

$$55x = 1\,100 \quad \text{(add 20 to both sides)}$$

$$x = 20 \quad \text{(divide both sides by 55)}$$

Notice the link between Geometry and Algebra in this question. This is an example of where the examiner can unify strands.

6 Solving Quadratic Equations

aims

- ☐ To learn how to solve a quadratic equation when given in many different forms.
- ☐ To be able to apply the methods for solving equations to in-context questions.

Any equation of the form $ax^2 + bx + c = 0$, $a \neq 0$, is called a quadratic equation. Solving a quadratic equation gives us the roots of the equation. These are the two values which satisfy the equation.

To solve a quadratic equation, factorise the expression, let each factor equal zero and solve.

key point

There are three different types of quadratic equation. It is vital for you to remember and be familiar with how to factorise each type. Methods of factorising were covered earlier in this book. It would be wise to revise these methods before continuing with this chapter.

Take out common terms	Difference of two squares	Factorise a trinomial
$x^2 + 2x = x(x + 2)$	$x^2 - 9 = (x + 3)(x - 3)$	$x^2 + 6x - 7 = (x - 1)(x + 7)$

Example

Solve the following quadratic equations:

(i) $2x^2 + 6x = 0$ (ii) $x^2 - 81 = 0$

Solution

(i) $\qquad 2x^2 + 6x = 0$

$\qquad 2x(x + 3) = 0$ (factorise)

(ii) $\qquad x^2 - 81 = 0$

$\qquad (x + 9)(x - 9) = 0$ (factorise)

$2x = 0$ or $x + 3 = 0$ | $x + 9 = 0$ or $x - 9 = 0$

$x = 0$ or $\quad x = -3$ (solve) | $\quad x = -9$ or $\quad x = 9$ (solve)

key point

These values for x are called the roots of the quadratic equation. These values are the points where the graph of the quadratic function crosses the x-axis. This is covered in detail in the chapter on Graphing Functions.

Example

Solve the following quadratic equations:

(i) $x^2 + 2x - 15 = 0$
(ii) $2x^2 + x - 10 = 0$

Solution

(i) $\qquad x^2 + 2x - 15 = 0$

$\qquad (x + 5)(x - 3) = 0$ (factorise)

$\quad x + 5 = 0$ or $x - 3 = 0$

$\qquad x = -5 \quad$ or $\quad x = 3$ (solve)

(ii) $\qquad 2x^2 + x - 10 = 0$

$\qquad (2x + 5)(x - 2) = 0$ (factorise)

$\quad 2x + 5 = 0$ or $x - 2 = 0$

$\qquad 2x = -5 \quad$ or $\quad x = 2$ (solve)

$$x = \frac{-5}{2} \quad \text{or} \quad x = 2$$

exam focus

It is a good idea to check your solutions in the original equation. In part (i) of this example:

$x = -5$: $(-5)^2 + 2(-5) - 15$ | $x = 3$: $(3)^2 + 2(3) - 15$

$\qquad\quad = 25 - 10 - 15$ | $\qquad\quad = 9 + 6 - 15$

$\qquad\quad = 0$ | $\qquad\quad = 0$

$\therefore x = -5$ is a solution | $\therefore x = 3$ is a solution

Example

Solve the following quadratic equations:

(i) $x^2 - 5x - 6 = 0$ (ii) $8x^2 - 14x + 3 = 0$

Solution

(i)
$$x^2 - 5x - 6 = 0$$
$$(x - 6)(x + 1) = 0 \quad \text{(factorise)}$$
$$x - 6 = 0 \text{ or } x + 1 = 0$$
$$x = 6 \text{ or } \quad x = -1$$

(ii)
$$8x^2 - 14x + 3 = 0$$
$$(4x - 1)(2x - 3) = 0 \text{(factorise)}$$
$$4x - 1 = 0 \text{ or } 2x - 3 = 0$$
$$4x = 1 \qquad 2x = 3$$
$$x = \frac{1}{4} \qquad x = \frac{3}{2}$$

exam Q

(i) Solve $n^2 - 13n + 36 = 0$.

(ii) Hence, find the two values of $t \in \mathbb{R}$ for which $(2t - 6)^2 - 13(2t - 6) + 36 = 0$.

exam focus

Remember, 'hence' in part (ii) means that you **must** use your solution from (i).

Solution

(i) $n^2 - 13n + 36 = 0$

$(n - 4)(n - 9) = 0$

$n - 4 = 0 \quad$ or $\quad n - 9 = 0$

$n = 4 \quad$ or $\qquad n = 9$

(ii) Comparing the equation in part (i) with the equation in part (ii):

$$n^2 - 13n + 36 = 0$$

$$(2t - 6)^2 - 13(2t - 6) + 36 = 0$$

n from the first equation $= 2t - 6$ in the second equation.

$$n = 2t - 6$$
$$4 = 2t - 6$$
$$4 + 6 = 2t$$
$$10 = 2t$$
$$5 = t$$

$$n = 2t - 6$$
$$9 = 2t - 6$$
$$9 + 6 = 2t$$
$$15 = 2t$$
$$7 \cdot 5 = t$$

key point

Notice that the structure of the equations from (i) and (ii) are the same. Both are in the form
$$(\;\;)^2 - 13(\;\;) + 36 = 0.$$

Example

The sides of a right-angled triangle are $3x$, $4x$ and $5x$ in length. The area of the triangle is $121{\cdot}5$ square units. Use this information to write an equation in x.

Solve the equation and hence find the lengths of the sides of the triangle.

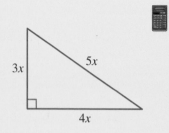

Solution

Area of a triangle $= \dfrac{1}{2}(\text{Base})(\perp \text{ Height})$

$$121{\cdot}5 = \frac{1}{2}(4x)(3x)$$

> **exam focus**
> Write the formula and fill in the information from the question. Then solve the equation to find the remaining variable.

$$2(121{\cdot}5) = 2\left[\frac{1}{2}(4x)(3x)\right] \quad \text{(multiply both sides by 2)}$$

$$243 = 12x^2$$

$$\frac{243}{12} = x^2 \qquad \text{(divide both sides by 12)}$$

$$\frac{81}{4} = x^2$$

$$\sqrt{\frac{81}{4}} = x$$

$$\pm\frac{9}{2} = x$$

$$\pm 4{\cdot}5 = x \qquad \text{(reject } x = -4{\cdot}5, \text{ as the lengths cannot be negative)}$$

$$\therefore\ 4{\cdot}5 = x$$

Sides are: $3x = 3(4{\cdot}5) = 13{\cdot}5$ units

$\qquad\qquad 4x = 4(4{\cdot}5) = 18$ units

$\qquad\qquad 5x = 5(4{\cdot}5) = 22{\cdot}5$ units

> **exam focus**
> If you get more than one answer it is important for you to look at which solutions make sense. Apply logic to determine which answers, if any, to reject.

A rectangular piece of cardboard has a length which is 8 cm more than its width, *w*. An open box is formed by cutting squares, whose side are 2 cm in length, from each corner of the rectangular piece of card, then folding up the sides.

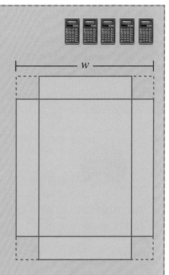

(i) Write the dimensions of the box in terms of *w*.

(ii) Find the dimensions of the box if its volume is 256 cm³.

Solution

(i) Width of cardboard = w

Length of cardboard = $w + 8$ (length is 8 cm more than the width)

Width of box = $w - 4$ (width minus 2 cm on each end)

Length of box = $w + 8 - 4 = w + 4$ (length minus 2 cm from each end)

(ii) Dimensions of the box are:

Width = $w - 4$, Length = $w + 4$, Height = 2

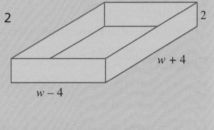

$$\text{Volume} = (\text{Length})(\text{Width})(\text{Height})$$
$$256 = (w + 4)(w - 4)(2)$$
$$256 = (w^2 - 4w + 4w - 16)(2)$$
$$256 = (w^2 - 16)(2)$$
$$256 = 2w^2 - 32$$
$$0 = 2w^2 - 288 \qquad \text{(divide both sides by 2)}$$
$$0 = w^2 - 144$$
$$0 = (w + 12)(w - 12) \qquad \text{(factorise)}$$

$w + 12 = 0$ or $w - 12 = 0$

$w = -12$ or $w = 12$

Reject $w = -12$, as lengths must always be positive.

Therefore, the dimensions of the box are:

Width = $w - 4$ = 8 cm   Length = $w + 4$ = 16 cm   and   Height = 2 cm

Final diagram:

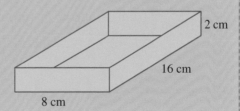

Constructing a quadratic equation when given its roots

Forming a quadratic equation is the opposite process to solving:

1. Let x equal each root.
2. Form the factors.
3. Multiply the factors by each other to form the equation.

key point

An alternative, and quicker, way to form a quadratic equation when given its roots is:

$$x^2 - (\text{sum of roots})x + (\text{product of roots}) = 0$$

You must learn and recall this formula if you want to use it. It is not in the booklet of formulae and tables.

Example

Form the quadratic equation with roots -2 and 4.

Solution

Roots -2 and 4

Let $x = -2$ and $x = 4$

$x + 2 = 0$ and $x - 4 = 0$ \qquad (form the factors)

$(x + 2)(x - 4) = 0$

$x^2 + 2x - 4x - 8 = 0$ \qquad (multiply the factors)

$x^2 - 2x - 8 = 0$ \qquad (simplify)

Alternative method: Find the sum of the roots and the product of the roots.

$$\text{Sum of roots} = -2 + 4 = 2$$
$$\text{Product of the roots} = (-2)(4) = -8$$

$$x^2 - (\text{sum of roots})x + (\text{product of roots}) = 0$$
$$x^2 - (2)x + (-8) = 0$$
$$x^2 - 2x - 8 = 0$$

Quadratic formula

In many quadratic equations, $ax^2 + bx + c$ cannot be resolved into factors. When this happens, the formula **must** be used. This formula is in the booklet of formulae and tables.

Note: The quadratic formula can be used to solve any quadratic equation, not only ones which cannot be factorised.

The roots of the quadratic equation $ax^2 + bx + c = 0$ are given by the formula

$$x = \frac{-b \pm \sqrt{b^2 - 4ac}}{2a}$$

(see booklet of formulae and tables)

Notes: 1. The whole of the top of the right-hand side, including $-b$, is divided by $2a$.

2. It is often called the $-b$ or quadratic formula.

3. Before using the formula, make sure every term is on the left-hand side, i.e. write the equation in the form $ax^2 + bx + c = 0$.

A clue that you must use the formula is often given in the question. When the question requires an approximate answer, e.g. 'correct to two decimal places', 'correct to three significant figures', 'correct to the nearest integer' or 'express your answer in surd form', then the formula must be used.

Example

Solve the following quadratic equations.

(i) $3x^2 - 5x - 13 = 0$, leaving your answer correct to one decimal place.

(ii) $2x^2 - 7x + 4 = 0$, leaving your answer in surd form.

Solution

(i) $3x^2 - 5x - 13 = 0$

$$x = \frac{-b \pm \sqrt{b^2 - 4ac}}{2a} \qquad (a = 3, b = -5, c = -13)$$

$$= \frac{-(-5) \pm \sqrt{(-5)^2 - 4(3)(-13)}}{2(3)}$$

$$= \frac{5 \pm \sqrt{25 + 156}}{6}$$

$$= \frac{5 \pm \sqrt{181}}{6}$$

key point

We are asked to leave the answers to one decimal place, so we know that we must use the formula.

Therefore, $\quad x = \dfrac{5 + \sqrt{181}}{6} = 3{\cdot}1 \quad$ or $\quad x = \dfrac{5 - \sqrt{181}}{6} = -1{\cdot}4$

(ii) $2x^2 - 7x + 4 = 0 \qquad (a = 2, b = -7, c = 4)$

$$x = \frac{-b \pm \sqrt{b^2 - 4ac}}{2a}$$

$$= \frac{-(-7) \pm \sqrt{(-7)^2 - 4(2)(4)}}{2(2)}$$

$$= \frac{7 \pm \sqrt{49 - 32}}{4}$$

$$= \frac{7 \pm \sqrt{17}}{4}$$

key point

We are asked to leave the answers in surd form, so we know that we must use the formula.

Therefore, $x = \dfrac{7 + \sqrt{17}}{4} \quad$ or $\quad x = \dfrac{7 - \sqrt{17}}{4}$

exam focus

Take care when b is a negative value.

$$-b = -(-7) = +7$$

(i) Solve the equation $x^2 - 6x + 4 = 0$, giving your answer in the form $a \pm \sqrt{b}$, where, $a, b \in \mathbb{N}$.

(ii) Hence or otherwise, find two values for p for which

$$(3 + p)^2 - 6(3 + p) + 4 = 0.$$

(iii) Show that the sum of the two values of p is zero.

Solution

(i) $x^2 - 6x + 4 = 0$ $\qquad\qquad (a = 1, b = -6, c = 4)$

$$x = \frac{b \pm \sqrt{b^2 - 4ac}}{2a}$$

$$x = \frac{-(-6) \pm \sqrt{(-6)^2 - 4(1)(4)}}{2(1)}$$

$$x = \frac{6 \pm \sqrt{36 - 16}}{2}$$

$$x = \frac{6 \pm \sqrt{20}}{2}$$

$$x = \frac{6 \pm 2\sqrt{5}}{2}$$

$$x = 3 \pm \sqrt{5}$$

(ii) Comparing the equation in part (i) with the equation in part (ii):

$$x^2 - 6x + 4 = 0$$

$$(3 + p)^2 - 6(3 + p) + 4 = 0$$

x from first equation equals $3 + p$ from second equation:

$$x = 3 + p \qquad\qquad\qquad\qquad x = 3 + p$$
$$3 + \sqrt{5} = 3 + p \qquad\qquad\quad 3 - \sqrt{5} = 3 + p$$
$$3 + \sqrt{5} - 3 = p \qquad\qquad\quad 3 - \sqrt{5} - 3 = p$$
$$\sqrt{5} = p \qquad\qquad\qquad\qquad -\sqrt{5} = p$$

(iii) Sum of the values for p = first value for p + second value for p

Sum of the values for $p = \sqrt{5} + (-\sqrt{5})$

Sum of the values for $p = \sqrt{5} - \sqrt{5}$

Sum of the values for $p = 0$

Verify that $3 - \sqrt{2}$ is a root (solution) of the equation $x^2 - 6x + 7 = 0$.

Solution

Solve the quadratic equation and see if one of the roots is $3 - \sqrt{2}$.

$x^2 - 6x + 7 = 0$

$$x = \frac{-b \pm \sqrt{b^2 - 4ac}}{2a}$$

$(a = 1, b = -6, c = 7)$

$$= \frac{-(-6) \pm \sqrt{(-6)^2 - 4(1)(7)}}{2(1)}$$

$$= \frac{6 \pm \sqrt{36 - 28}}{2}$$

$$= \frac{6 \pm \sqrt{8}}{2}$$

$$= \frac{6 \pm 2\sqrt{2}}{2}$$

$$= 3 \pm \sqrt{2}$$

$x = 3 + \sqrt{2}$ or $x = 3 - \sqrt{2}$

We can also verify a root by substituting it into the equation. If it satisfies the equation (i.e. the left side equals the right side), then it is a root. Otherwise it is not.

Thus, we have verified that $3 - \sqrt{2}$ is a root of the equation $x^2 - 6x + 7 = 0$.

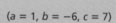

The lengths of the sides of a right-angled triangle are shown in the diagram.

(i) Using the theorem of Pythagoras, write an equation in x.

(ii) Solve this equation to find x correct to two decimal places.

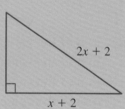

Solution

(i) Using the theorem of Pythagoras:

$$c^2 = a^2 + b^2$$
$$(2x + 2)^2 = (x + 1)^2 + (x + 2)^2$$
$$4x^2 + 8x + 4 = x^2 + 2x + 1 + x^2 + 4x + 4$$
$$4x^2 + 8x + 4 = 2x^2 + 6x + 5$$
$$2x^2 + 2x - 1 = 0$$

(ii) Solving:

$$2x^2 + 2x - 1 = 0$$

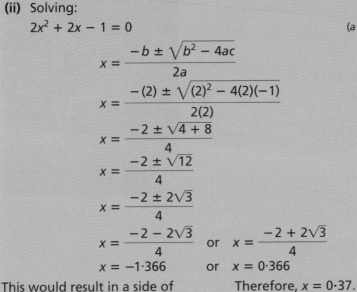

$(a = 2, b = 2, c = -1)$

$$x = \frac{-b \pm \sqrt{b^2 - 4ac}}{2a}$$

$$x = \frac{-(2) \pm \sqrt{(2)^2 - 4(2)(-1)}}{2(2)}$$

$$x = \frac{-2 \pm \sqrt{4 + 8}}{4}$$

$$x = \frac{-2 \pm \sqrt{12}}{4}$$

$$x = \frac{-2 \pm 2\sqrt{3}}{4}$$

$$x = \frac{-2 - 2\sqrt{3}}{4} \quad \text{or} \quad x = \frac{-2 + 2\sqrt{3}}{4}$$

$$x = -1{\cdot}366 \quad \text{or} \quad x = 0{\cdot}366$$

This would result in a side of negative length, so we reject this result.

Therefore, $x = 0{\cdot}37$.

exam focus

If you get more than one answer it is important for you to look at which solutions make sense. Apply logic to determine which answers, if any, to reject.

A diver jumps from a platform that is 10 m high. The height of the diver above the water t seconds after jumping is given by:

$$h = -4.9t^2 + 3.2t + 10.5$$

(i) Find the height of the diver after 1·5 seconds.

(ii) Find, to the nearest hundredth of a second, how long after jumping it will take for the diver to hit the water.

Solution

(i) Find height, h, when $t = 1.5$ seconds:

$h = -4.9t^2 + 3.2t + 10.5$

$h = -4.9(1.5)^2 + 3.2(1.5) + 10.5$

$h = -11.025 + 4.8 + 10.5$

$h = 4.275$ m

Therefore, the diver is 4·275 m above the water after 1·5 seconds.

(ii) When the diver hits the water, her height is 0 m. Thus, we need to find t when $h = 0$.

$h = -4.9t^2 + 3.2t + 10.5$

$0 = -4.9t^2 + 3.2t + 10.5$

Use the quadratic formula, where $a = -4.9$, $b = 3.2$ and $c = 10.5$.

$$t = \frac{-b \pm \sqrt{b^2 - 4ac}}{2a}$$

$$= \frac{-(3.2) \pm \sqrt{(3.2)^2 - 4(-4.9)(10.5)}}{2(-4.9)}$$

$$= \frac{-3.2 \pm \sqrt{10.24 + 205.8}}{-9.8}$$

$$= \frac{-3.2 \pm \sqrt{216.04}}{-9.8}$$

$$\therefore \; t = \frac{-3.2 + \sqrt{216.04}}{-9.8} \qquad \text{or} \qquad t = \frac{-3.2 - \sqrt{216.04}}{-9.8}$$

$$t = -1.17 \qquad\qquad\qquad\qquad t = 1.82636$$

She jumped at $t = 0$ sec, and so the solution cannot be a negative value.

Therefore, the time to hit the water is 1·83 sec to the nearest one-hundredth of a second.

> **exam focus**
>
> Write down what values you have and what you want, in terms of the variables used.

7 Simultaneous Equations

☐ To learn how to use suitable strategies for finding solutions to simultaneous linear equations with two unknowns.

☐ To learn how to interpret the results from solving two equations simultaneously.

Simultaneous linear equations with two unknowns

Simultaneous linear equations in two variables are solved with the following steps:

1. Write both equations in the form $ax + by = k$ and label the equations ① and ②.

2. Multiply one or both of the equations by a number in order to make the coefficients of x or y the same, but of opposite sign.

3. Add to remove the variable with equal coefficients but of opposite sign.

4. Solve the resultant equation to find the value of the remaining unknown (x or y).

5. Substitute this value in equation ① or ② to find the value of the other unknown.

key point

Solution containing fractions: If the answer at step 4 is a fraction, the substitution might be difficult. In such cases, you can repeat steps 1 to 4 for the other variable.

Example

Solve the following pair of simultaneous equations:
$$2x + y = 72 \quad \text{and} \quad x - y = -27$$

Solution

To eliminate the ys:

$2x + y = 72$

$\underline{x - y = -27}$ (add the rows)

$3x = 45$ (÷ 3)

$x = 15$

To find the value for y, let $x = 15$ in either of the equations:

$$2x + y = 72$$
$$2(15) + y = 72$$
$$30 + y = 72$$
$$y = 42$$

Therefore, the solution is $x = 15, y = 42$.

Example

Solve the following pair of simultaneous equations:

$$2x + 3y = 5 \quad \text{and} \quad x - 4y = -14$$

Solution

To eliminate the xs:

$$2x + 3y = 5$$
$$\underline{x - 4y = -14} \quad (\times -2)$$
$$2x + 3y = 5$$
$$\underline{-2x + 8y = 28} \quad \text{(add the rows)}$$
$$11y = 33 \quad (\div 11)$$
$$y = 3$$

To find the value for x, let $y = 3$ in either of the equations:

$$2x + 3y = 5$$
$$2x + 3(3) = 5$$
$$2x + 9 = 5$$
$$2x = -4$$
$$x = -2$$

Therefore, the solution is $x = -2, y = 3$.

Solve the following pair of simultaneous equations:

$$5a + b = 1 \quad \text{and} \quad 2a + 3b = -10$$

key point

Equations do not always have to be in terms of x and y.

Solution

To eliminate the bs:

$$5a + b = 1 \quad (\times -3)$$
$$\underline{2a + 3b = -10}$$
$$-15a - 3b = -3$$
$$\underline{2a + 3b = -10} \quad \text{(add the rows)}$$
$$-13a = -13 \quad (\div -13)$$
$$a = 1$$

To find the value for b, let $a = 1$ in either of the equations:

$$5a + b = 1$$
$$5(1) + b = 1$$
$$5 + b = 1$$
$$b = -4$$

Therefore, the solution is $a = 1, b = -4$.

(i) Solve the simultaneous equations:

$$3x + 4y = -1 \quad \text{and} \quad 2x + 9 = -6y$$

(ii) By graphing the two lines on a single coordinate diagram, check your answer to part **(i)**.

Solution

(i) Solve the simultaneous equations:

$$3x + 4y = -1$$
$$2x + 9 = -6y$$

$$3x + 4y = -1 \quad (\times 2)$$
$$\underline{2x + 6y = -9} \quad (\times -3)$$
$$6x + 8y = -2 \quad (\times 2)$$
$$\underline{-6x - 18y = 27} \quad (\times -3)$$
$$-10y = 25 \quad (\div -10)$$
$$y = -2 \cdot 5$$

To find the value for x, let $y = -2 \cdot 5$ in either of the equations:

$$3x + 4(-2 \cdot 5) = -1$$
$$3x - 10 = -1$$
$$3x = 9$$
$$x = 3$$

Therefore, the solution is $x = 3$, $y = -2 \cdot 5$.

(ii) To graph the lines, we need to find the points where they cross the x- and y-axes.

For $3x + 4y = -1$:

At the x-axis, $y = 0$:

$$3x + 4(0) = -1$$
$$3x = -1$$
$$x = \frac{-1}{3}$$

Point: $\left(-\frac{1}{3}, 0\right)$

At the y-axis, $x = 0$:

$$3(0) + 4y = -1$$
$$4y = -1$$
$$y = \frac{-1}{4}$$

Point: $\left(0, -\frac{1}{4}\right)$

For $2x + 9 = -6y$:

At the x-axis, $y = 0$:

$$2x + 9 = -6(0)$$
$$2x + 9 = 0$$
$$2x = -9$$
$$x = -4 \cdot 5$$

Point: $(-4 \cdot 5, 0)$

At the y-axis, $x = 0$:

$$2(0) + 9 = -6y$$
$$9 = -6y$$
$$\frac{9}{-6} = y$$
$$-1 \cdot 5 = y$$

Point: $(0, -1 \cdot 5)$

Graphing the lines

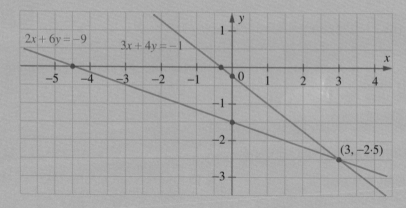

From the graph we can see that the point of intersection is (3, −2·5). This agrees with the answer from part **(i)**.

Notice the link here between Algebra and Coordinate Geometry of the Line. Coordinate Geometry of the Line is covered in detail in the *Less Stress More Success Junior Cycle Maths Book 2*.

Simultaneous linear equations with fractions

Where necessary, multiply the equations across by the common denominator. Then rearrange to get the equations in the form:

$$ax + by = c$$

Example

Solve the simultaneous equations:

$$\frac{1}{3}f + \frac{1}{2}g = 0 \quad \text{and} \quad -\frac{11}{6}f + \frac{1}{4}g = -6$$

Solution

Get the equations in the form $ax + by = c$.

Equation 1:   Multiply $\frac{1}{3}f + \frac{1}{2}g = 0$ by 6.

$$6\left(\frac{1}{3}f\right) + 6\left(\frac{1}{2}g\right) = 6(0)$$

$$2f + 3g = 0$$

Equation 2:   Multiply $-\frac{11}{6}f + \frac{1}{4}g = -6$ by 12.

$$12\left(-\frac{11}{6}f\right) + 12\left(\frac{1}{4}g\right) = 12(-6)$$

$$-22f + 3g = -72$$

Now solve the equations.

Eliminate the gs:

$$2f + 3g = 0$$

$$\underline{-22f + 3g = -72} \qquad (\times -1)$$

$$2f + 3g = 0$$

$$\underline{22f - 3g = 72}$$

$$24f = 72 \qquad (\div 24)$$

$$f = 3$$

To find the value for g, let $f = 3$ in either of the equations:

$$2f + 3g = 0$$

$$2(3) + 3g = 0$$

$$6 + 3g = 0$$

$$3g = -6$$

$$g = -2$$

Therefore, the solution is $f = 3, g = -2$.

Solve the equations for p and q:

$$\frac{2p-5}{3} + \frac{q}{5} = 6; \qquad \frac{3p}{10} + 2 = \frac{3q-5}{2}$$

Solution

Equation 1:
$$\frac{2p-5}{3} + \frac{q}{5} = 6$$

$$15\left(\frac{2p-5}{3}\right) + 15\left(\frac{q}{5}\right) = 15(6) \quad (\times 15)$$

$$5(2p-5) + 3(q) = 15(6)$$

$$10p - 25 + 3q = 90$$

$$10p + 3q = 115 \quad ①$$

Equation 2:
$$\frac{3p}{10} + 2 = \frac{3q-5}{2}$$

$$10\left(\frac{3p}{10}\right) + 10(2) = 10\left(\frac{3q-5}{2}\right) \quad (\times 10)$$

$$1(3p) + 10(2) = 5(3q - 5)$$

$$3p + 20 = 15q - 25$$

$$3p - 15q = -45 \quad ②$$

Now solve ① and ②:

$$10p + 3q = 115 \quad (\times 5)$$
$$\underline{3p - 15q = -45}$$
$$50p + 15q = 575$$
$$\underline{3p - 15q = -45}$$
$$53p = 530 \quad (\div 53)$$
$$p = 10$$

Sub $x = 10$ into ①:

$$10(10) + 3q = 115$$
$$100 + 3q = 115$$
$$3q = 15 \quad (\div 5)$$
$$q = 5$$

Answers: $p = 10$　and　$q = 5$

Using simultaneous equations in real-world scenarios

Read the given information carefully and use it to form two equations. Then solve these equations simultaneously.

Jodie makes a solid shape using equilateral triangles as faces. It has E edges and F faces, where $E, F \in \mathbb{N}$. For Jodie's shape

$$\frac{8F}{5} - E = 2$$

$$3F = 2E$$

Solve these simultaneous equations to find the value of E and the value of F.

Solution

Equation 1:

$$\frac{8F}{5} - E = 2 \qquad \times 5$$

$$8F - 5E = 10 \qquad ①$$

Equation 2:

$$3F = 2E$$

$$3F - 2E = 0 \qquad ②$$

Now solve equations ① and ②

$$\begin{aligned} 8F - 5E &= 10 \qquad \text{(multiply by 2)} \\ 3F - 2E &= 0 \qquad \text{(multiply by } -5\text{)} \\ 16F - 10E &= 20 \\ -15F + 10E &= 0 \\ \hline F &= 20 \end{aligned}$$

Find E:

$$\begin{aligned} 3F &= 2E \\ 3(20) &= 2E \\ 60 &= 2E \\ 30 &= E \end{aligned}$$

Example

An examination paper consists of 40 questions.

5 marks are given for each correct answer.

3 marks are deducted for each incorrect answer.

Kenny answered all 40 questions, getting x correct and getting y incorrect. His total score for the examination was 56 marks.

(i) Write two equations to represent the above information.

(ii) Solve these equations to find how many questions Kenny answered correctly.

Solution

(i) Total number of questions $= x + y$

$$40 = x + y$$

Total marks $= 5(x) + (-3)(y)$

$$56 = 5x - 3y$$

(ii) Solve the equations:

$$x + y = 40 \quad (\times 3)$$

$$5x - 3y = 56$$

$$\overline{}$$

$$3x + 3y = 120$$

$$5x - 3y = 56$$

$$\overline{}$$

$$8x = 176$$

$$x = 22$$

Let $x = 22$:

$$x + y = 40$$

$$22 + y = 40$$

$$y = 40 - 22$$

$$y = 18$$

Therefore, Kenny answered 22 questions correctly and 18 questions incorrectly.

Suzanne is saving for Christmas. Throughout the year she collects savings stamps at the post office. By December she has €25 saved. This is made up of 20 cent saving stamps and 50 cent saving stamps. She has 104 saving stamps in total.

(i) Taking x to be the number of 20 cent saving stamps and y to be the number of 50 cent saving stamps, write down two equations in x and y to represent this information.

(ii) Solve the equations to find the number of each type of stamp Suzanne has.

Solution

(i) Total number of stamps $= x + y$

$$104 = x + y$$

Value of stamps in cent $= 20(x) + 50(y)$

$$2{,}500 = 20x + 50y$$

$$250 = 2x + 5y$$

(ii) Solve the equations:

$$x + y = 104 \quad (\times -2)$$
$$2x + 5y = 250$$
$$-2x - 2y = -208$$
$$2x + 5y = 250$$
$$3y = 42$$
$$y = 14$$

Let $y = 14$
$$x + y = 104$$
$$x + 14 = 104$$
$$x = 90$$

Therefore, Suzanne has ninety 20 cent saving stamps and fourteen 50 cent saving stamps.

Notice that in this question you were given information in both euro and cent. You must convert them to be the same units. If you are given two different units of measure, it is important to convert one of them before beginning the question. This issue occurs in other areas of the course too, for example Area and Volume.

A company employs two drivers, John and David. Each has the use of a company car and small van. The company buys €30 worth of Toll Tags for each driver. Each time that a vehicle goes through the M50 toll, a charge will be deducted from the Toll Tags.

John goes through the M50 toll five times in his car and four times in his small van. He then has €7·90 remaining on his Toll Tags.

David goes through the M50 toll twice in his car and six times in his small van. He then has €8·40 left on his Toll Tags.

Calculate how much it costs for a car and for a small van to go through the M50 toll.

Solution

Let x = cost of a car and y = cost of a van.

John: 5(cost of a car) + 4(cost of van) = €30 − €7·90

$$5x + 4y = 22\cdot10$$

David: 2(cost of a car) + 6(cost of a van) = €30 − €8·40

$$2x + 6y = 21\cdot60$$

exam focus

You were not told to form two simultaneous equations. You are expected to know to do this.

Solving: $5x + 4y = 22\cdot10$ (×3)

$\underline{2x + 6y = 21\cdot60}$ (×−2)

$15x + 12y = 66\cdot30$

$\underline{-4x - 12y = -43\cdot20}$

$11x = 23\cdot10$

$x = 2\cdot10$

Let $x = 2\cdot10$:

$5x + 4y = 22\cdot10$

$5(2\cdot10) + 4y = 22\cdot10$

$10\cdot50 + 4y = 22\cdot10$

$4y = 11\cdot60$

$y = 2\cdot90$

Therefore, the toll for a car = €2·10 and the toll for a van = €2·90.

8 Long Division in Algebra

Long division in algebra follows the same procedure as long division in arithmetic. The stages in dividing one algebraic expression by another are shown in the following examples.

Example

The area of a rectangle is $2x^2 + 7x - 15$.
If one of the sides is $(x + 5)$, find the other side.

$$? \boxed{\begin{array}{c} x + 5 \\ 2x^2 + 7x - 15 \end{array}}$$

Solution

$$\text{Area} = \text{Length} \times \text{Width}$$
$$2x^2 + 7x - 15 = (x + 5)(\text{Width})$$

Method 1: Factorise $2x^2 + 7x - 15$.
$$(2x - 3)(x + 5)$$

Therefore, Width $= 2x - 3$

Method 2: Divide $2x^2 + 7x - 15$ by $x + 5$.

$$
\begin{array}{r}
2x - 3 \\
x + 5 \overline{\smash{\big)}\, 2x^2 + 7x - 15} \\
\underline{2x^2 + 10x} \quad\downarrow \\
-3x - 15 \\
\underline{-3x - 15} \\
0
\end{array}
$$

$(2x^2 \div x = 2x,$ put $2x$ on top$)$
$(2x(x + 5) = 2x^2 + 10x)$
(Subtract and bring down $-15.$ $-3x \div x = -3)$
$(-3(x + 5) = -3x - 15)$
(subtract)

Therefore, $2x^2 + 7x - 15 \div x + 5 = 2x - 3$.

Therefore, the width of the rectangle $= 2x - 3$.

Example

Divide $x^3 + x^2 - 12x$ by $x + 4$.

Solution

$$
\begin{array}{r}
x^2 - 3x \\
x + 4 \overline{\smash{\big)}\, x^3 + x^2 - 12x} \\
\underline{x^3 + 4x^2} \quad\downarrow \\
-3x^2 - 12x \\
\underline{-3x^2 - 12x} \\
0
\end{array}
$$

($x^3 \div x = x^2$, put x^2 on top)

($x^2(x + 4) = x^3 + 4x^2$)

(Subtract and bring down $-12x$. $-3x^2 \div x = -3x$)

($-3x(x + 4) = -3x^2 - 12x$)

(subtract)

Therefore, $(x^3 + x^2 - 12x) \div (x + 4) = x^2 - 3x$.

key point

The result at the bottom is the remainder and it must always be zero. The solution to the question is at the top of the sum.

Example

Divide $2x^3 + 5x^2 - 14x + 3$ by $2x - 3$.

Solution

$$
\begin{array}{r}
x^2 + 4x - 1 \\
2x - 3 \overline{\smash{\big)}\, 2x^3 + 5x^2 - 14x + 3} \\
\underline{2x^3 - 3x^2} \quad\downarrow \\
8x^2 - 14x \\
\underline{8x^2 - 12x} \quad\downarrow \\
-2x + 3 \\
\underline{-2x + 3} \\
0
\end{array}
$$

($2x^3 \div 2x = x^2$, put x^2 on top)

($x^2(2x - 3) = 2x^3 - 3x^2$)

(Subtract and bring down $-14x$. $8x^2 \div 2x = 4x$)

($4x(2x - 3) = 8x^2 - 12x$)

(Subtract and bring down 3. $-2x \div 2x = -1$)

($-1(2x - 3) = -2x + 3$)

(subtract)

Therefore, $(2x^3 + 5x^2 - 14x + 3) \div (2x - 3) = x^2 + 4x - 1$.

Divide $6x^3 - 13x^2 + 27x - 14$ by $3x - 2$.

Solution

$$
\begin{array}{r}
2x^2 - 3x + 7 \\
3x - 2 \,\overline{\smash{\big)}\, 6x^3 - 13x^2 + 27x - 14}
\end{array}
$$

$\underline{6x^3 - 4x^2}$ $\downarrow$

$-9x^2 + 27x$

$\underline{-9x^2 + 6x}$

$21x - 14$

$\underline{21x - 14}$

0

($6x^3 \div 3x = 2x^2$, put $2x^2$ on top)

($2x^2(3x - 2) = 6x^3 - 4x^2$)

(Subtract and bring down $27x$. $-9x^2 \div 3x = -3x$)

($-3x(3x - 2) = -9x^2 + 6x$)

(Subtract and bring down -14. $21x \div 3x = 7$)

($7(3x - 2) = 21x - 14$)

(subtract)

Therefore, $(6x^3 - 13x^2 + 27x - 14) \div (3x - 2) = 2x^2 - 3x + 7$.

Example

Divide $4x^3 - 13x - 6$ by $x - 2$.

key point

There is no x^2 term, so we must add in $0x^2$, otherwise the columns of terms won't line up correctly.

Solution

$$
\begin{array}{r}
4x^2 + 8x + 3 \\
x - 2 \,\overline{\smash{\big)}\, 4x^3 + 0x^2 - 13x - 6}
\end{array}
$$

$\underline{4x^3 - 8x^2}$ $\downarrow$

$8x^2 - 13x$

$\underline{8x^2 - 16x}$

$3x - 6$

$\underline{3x - 6}$

0

($4x^3 \div x = 4x^2$, put $2x^2$ on top)

($4x^2(x - 2) = 4x^3 - 8x^2$)

(Subtract and bring down $-13x$. $8x^2 \div x = 8x$)

($8x(x - 2) = 8x^2 - 16x$)

(Subtract and bring down -6. $3x \div x = 3$)

($3(x - 2) = 3x - 6$)

(subtract)

Therefore, $(4x^3 - 13x - 6) \div (x - 2) = 4x^2 + 8x + 3$.

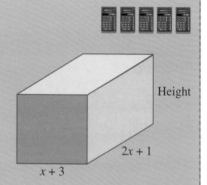

The diagram shows a rectangular box.
It has a length of $2x + 1$ and a width of $x + 3$.

Given that the volume of the box is
$2x^3 + 5x^2 - 4x - 3$, find the height of the box.

Solution

Volume of a box = Length × Width × Height

$$\frac{\text{Volume of box}}{(\text{Length})(\text{Width})} = \text{Height}$$

$$\frac{2x^3 + 5x^2 - 4x - 3}{(2x + 1)(x + 3)} = \text{Height}$$

$$\frac{2x^3 + 5x^2 - 4x - 3}{2x^2 + 7x + 3} = \text{Height}$$

Division:

$$
\begin{array}{r}
x - 1 \\
2x^2 + 7x + 3 \overline{\smash{\big)}\, 2x^3 + 5x^2 - 4x - 3}
\end{array}
$$

$\underline{2x^3 + 7x^2 + 3x}$ ↓   (subtract bottom row from top)

$-2x^2 - 7x - 3$

$\underline{-2x^2 - 7x - 3}$ (subtract bottom row from top)

0

Therefore, the height of the box = $x - 1$.

aims

☐ To learn how to solve linear inequalities.
☐ To learn how to graph a solution set on a number line.
☐ To be able to apply inequality methods to in-context questions.

The four inequality symbols are:

1. $>$ means greater than   **2.** $\geq$ means greater than or equal to

3. $<$ means less than   **4.** $\leq$ means less than or equal to

Algebraic expressions that are linked by one of the four inequality symbols are called **inequalities**. For example, $3x - 1 \geq 11$ and $-3 < 2x - 1$ are inequalities.
Solving inequalities is exactly the same as solving equations, with the following exception:

key point

Multiplying or dividing both sides of an inequality by a **negative** number **reverses** the direction of the inequality symbol.

That is:

$>$ changes to $<$ $\geq$ changes to $\leq$

$<$ changes to $>$ $\leq$ changes to $\geq$

Solving an inequality means finding the values of x that make the inequality true.
The following rules apply to graphing inequalities on a number line:

Number line for $x \in \mathbb{N}$ or $x \in \mathbb{Z}$, use **dots**.

Number line for $x \in \mathbb{R}$, use a **full** heavy line.

Note: Inequalities can be turned around. For example:

$5 \leq x$ means the same as $x \geq 5$

$8 \geq x \geq 3$ means the same as $3 \leq x \leq 8$

(see booklet of formulae and tables)

It is vital that you are familiar with the basic **number systems:**

$\mathbb{N} = \{1, 2, 3, \ldots\}$, the set of natural numbers.

$\mathbb{Z} = \{\ldots -2, -1, 0, 1, 2, \ldots\}$, the set of integers.

$\mathbb{R}$ = All whole numbers, decimals, rational and irrational numbers are known as the set of real numbers.

Inequalities in one variable

Example

Graph on the number line the solution set of $3x - 5 \leq x + 7, x \in \mathbb{N}$.

Solution

$$3x - 5 \leq x + 7$$
$$3x - 5 - x \leq 7 \qquad \text{(subtract } x \text{ from both sides)}$$
$$3x - x \leq 7 + 5 \qquad \text{(add 5 to both sides)}$$
$$2x \leq 12 \qquad \text{(simplify)}$$
$$x \leq 6 \qquad \text{(divide both sides by 2)}$$

As $x \in \mathbb{N}$, this is the set of natural numbers less than or equal to 6.
Thus, the values of x are 1, 2, 3, 4, 5 and 6.

Number line:

Note: As $x \in \mathbb{N}$, dots are used on the number line.

Find the largest possible value of n such that $5n + 48 > 8n - 6, n \in \mathbb{N}$.

Solution

$$5n + 48 > 8n - 6$$
$$48 + 6 > 8n - 5n \qquad \text{(subtract } 5n \text{ and add 6 to both sides)}$$
$$54 > 3n \qquad \text{(simplify)}$$
$$18 > n \qquad \text{(divide both sides by 3)}$$

Since $n \in \mathbb{N}$, n is a positive whole number.
The largest positive whole number less than 18 is 17.
Therefore, the largest value of n is 17.

Example

Graph on the number line the solution set of $-2x + 1 > -9, x \in \mathbb{Z}$.

Solution

$-2x + 1 > -9$

$\qquad -2x > -9 - 1 \qquad$ (subtract 1 from both sides)

$\qquad -2x > -10 \qquad$ (simplify)

$\qquad 2x < 10 \qquad$ (multiply both sides by -1 and reverse the direction of the inequality)

$\qquad x < 5 \qquad$ (divide both sides by 2)

As $x \in \mathbb{Z}$, this is the set of integers (whole numbers) less than 5.

Thus, the values of x are 4, 3, 2, 1, 0, -1, -2, etc.

Number line:

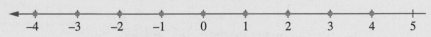

Note: As $x \in \mathbb{Z}$, dots are used on the number line.

Example

Find the solution set of $11 - 3x \geq 2$, $x \in \mathbb{N}$ and graph your solution on the number line.

Solution

$11 - 3x \geq 2$

$\qquad -3x \geq -9 \qquad$ (subtract 11 from both sides)

$\qquad 3x \leq 9 \qquad$ (multiply both sides by -1 and reverse the direction of the inequality)

$\qquad x \leq 3 \qquad$ (divide both sides by 3)

As $x \in \mathbb{N}$, this is the set of natural numbers less than or equal to 3.

Thus, the values of x are 1, 2 and 3.

Number line:

Note: As $x \in \mathbb{N}$, dots are used on the number line.

Find the range of values of $x \in \mathbb{R}$ for which $4(x - 2) > 5(2x - 1) - 9$ and graph your solution on the number line.

Solution

$$4(x - 2) > 5(2x - 1) - 9$$

$$4x - 8 > 10x - 5 - 9 \qquad \text{(remove the brackets)}$$

$$4x - 10x > -5 - 9 + 8 \qquad \text{(subtract 10x and add 8 to both sides)}$$

$$-6x > -6 \qquad \text{(simplify both sides)}$$

$$6x < 6 \qquad \text{(multiply both sides by } -1 \text{ and reverse the inequality)}$$

$$x < 1 \qquad \text{(divide both sides by 6)}$$

Number line:

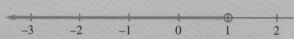

Note: 1. As $x \in \mathbb{R}$, we use full heavy shading on the number line.

   2. A hollow circle is put around 1 to indicate that it is **not** included in the solution.

key point

The inequality is $<$ and not $\leq$, so you must put a circle on the number line and not a dot.

Example

(i) Find the solution set P of $2x + 9 \leq 13, x \in \mathbb{R}$.

(ii) Find the solution set Q of $4 - 2x < 10, x \in \mathbb{R}$.

(iii) Find $P \cap Q$ and graph your solution on the number line.

Solution

We solve each inequality separately and then combine the solutions.

(i) P: $2x + 9 \leq 13$ (ii) Q: $4 - 2x < 10$

$\qquad\qquad 2x \leq 4$ $\qquad\qquad -2x < 6$

$\qquad\qquad\ x \leq 2$ $\qquad\qquad\quad 2x > -6$

$\qquad\qquad\qquad\qquad\qquad\qquad\qquad\qquad\qquad\ x > -3$

(iii) Combining the two inequalities gives:

$$P \cap Q: \quad -3 < x \leq 2, x \in \mathbb{R}$$

This is the set of positive and negative real numbers between -3 and 2, including 2 but not including -3.

We were not asked to draw the number lines in parts (i) and (ii), but as you can see from below, these number lines are helpful when plotting the final solution set:

(i) $P: x \leq 2$

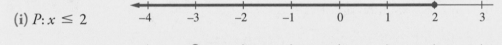

(ii) $Q: x > -3$

$P \cap Q: -3 < x \leq 2$

Note: 1. As $x \in \mathbb{R}$, we use full heavy shading on the number line.
2. A hollow circle is put around -3 to indicate that it is **not** included in the solution.
3. A dot is put on 2 to indicate that it **is** included in the solution.

Students often have difficulty determining the correct region for the final answer. Spend some time practising this.

Sharon calls A1 Towing to tow her car after it broke down. A1 Towing charges a €75·00 call out fee and €3·00 per kilometre after the first 10 kilometres towed. Let k be the number of kilometres towed over 10 km.

(i) Sharon can afford to spend no more than €115 towing her car. Write an inequality in terms of k to represent this information.

(ii) Solve the inequality from (i) and hence find the total maximum number of whole kilometres Sharon can get her car towed.

Solution

(i) (Call out charge) + (Charge per km over 10 km) ≤ 115
$$(75) + (3k) \leq 115$$

(ii) $(75) + (3k) \leq 115$
$$3k \leq 115 - 75$$
$$3k \leq 40$$
$$k \leq 13 \cdot 333333$$

Therefore, Sharon can get her car towed 13 km over the 10 km, so she can get her car towed a total distance of 23 km.

(i) Find A, the solution set of $3x - 5 < 7$, $x \in \mathbb{Z}$.

(ii) Find B, the solution set of $\dfrac{-2-3x}{4} \leq 1$, $x \in \mathbb{Z}$.

(iii) List the elements of $A \cap B$.

Solution

(i) $3x - 5 < 7$

$\qquad 3x < 7 + 5$ $\qquad$ (add 5 to both sides)

$\qquad 3x < 12$

$\qquad x < 4$ $\qquad$ (divide both sides by 3)

Therefore, set A contains all integers less than 4.

$A = \{3, 2, 1, 0, -1, -2, -3, -4, \ldots\}$

(ii) $\qquad \dfrac{-2 - 3x}{4} \leq 1$

$\qquad 4\left(\dfrac{-2 - 3x}{4}\right) \leq 4(1)$ $\qquad$ (multiply both sides by 4)

$\qquad -2 - 3x \leq 4$

$\qquad -2 - 4 \leq 3x$ $\qquad$ (subtract 4 and add 3x to both sides)

$\qquad -6 \leq 3x$ $\qquad$ (simplify)

$\qquad -2 \leq x$ $\qquad$ (divide both sides by 3)

Therefore, set B contains all integers greater than or equal to -2.

$B = \{-2, -1, 0, 1, 2, 3, 4, 5, 6, \ldots\}$

(iii) To find $A \cap B$ we must combine the two inequalities: $A \cap B = -2 \leq x < 4$.

Therefore, the elements of $A \cap B$ are $\{-2, -1, 0, 1, 2, 3\}$.

Notice the difference between making a list of elements and drawing a number line.

The width of a rectangle is x cm and its length is $(2x - 3)$ cm, where $x \in \mathbb{N}$.

(i) If the perimeter of the rectangle must be greater than 42 cm, find the smallest possible value of x.

(ii) Hence, find the area of the rectangle for this value of x.

x cm

$(2x - 3)$ cm

Solution

(i)

$$\text{Perimeter} > 42$$
$$2(\text{Length}) + 2(\text{Width}) > 42$$
$$2(2x - 3) + 2(x) > 42$$
$$4x - 6 + 2x > 42$$
$$6x - 6 > 42$$
$$6x > 48$$
$$x > 8$$

Therefore, the smallest possible value of x is 9 cm.

(ii) If $x = 9$:

Width = 9 and Length = $2(9) - 3 = 15$

Area = Length × Width

Area = 9 × 15

Area = 135 cm^2

10 Indices, Index Notation and Irrational Numbers

aims

- ☐ To become familiar with the rules of indices.
- ☐ To learn how to use the rules of indices to solve problems.
- ☐ To understand index notation.
- ☐ To be able to work with index notation when solving problems.
- ☐ To learn how to add, subtract and multiply irrational numbers.

In the expression a^m, a is the base and m is the index.

The index can also be called the power or the exponent.

key point

a^m is read as 'a to the power of m'.

Rules of Indices

Where $a, b \in \mathbb{R}$; $p, q \in \mathbb{Q}$; $a, b \neq 0$:

Rule (see booklet of tables and formulae)	Example	
1. $a^p a^q = a^{p+q}$	$5^4 5^3 = 5^{4+3} = 5^7$	$x^3 x^5 = x^{3+5} = x^8$
2. $\dfrac{a^p}{a^q} = a^{p-q}$	$\dfrac{3^5}{3^2} = 3^{5-2} = 3^3$	$\dfrac{x^7}{x^3} = x^{7-3} = x^4$
3. $(a^p)^q = a^{pq}$	$(3^2)^4 = 3^8$	$(x^3)^4 = x^{12}$
4. $a^0 = 1$	$7^0 = 1$	$x^0 = 1$
5. $a^{-p} = \dfrac{1}{a^p}$	$4^{-2} = \dfrac{1}{4^2}$	$x^{-3} = \dfrac{1}{x^3}$
6. $a^{\frac{1}{q}} = \sqrt[q]{a}$ $q \in \mathbb{Z}, q \neq 0, a > 0$	$5^{\frac{1}{3}} = \sqrt[3]{5}$	$x^{\frac{1}{2}} = \sqrt[2]{x} = \sqrt{x}$
7. $a^{\frac{p}{q}} = \sqrt[q]{a^p} = (\sqrt[q]{a})^p$ $p, q \in \mathbb{Z}, q \neq 0, a > 0$	$9^{\frac{2}{3}} = \sqrt[3]{9^2} = (\sqrt[3]{9})^2$	$x^{\frac{2}{5}} = \sqrt[5]{x^2} = (\sqrt[5]{x})^2$
8. $(ab)^p = a^p b^p$	$(2x)^3 = 2^3 x^3 = 8x^3$	$(xy)^5 = x^5 y^5$
9. $\left(\dfrac{a}{b}\right)^p = \dfrac{a^p}{b^p}$	$\left(\dfrac{3}{5}\right)^2 = \dfrac{3^2}{5^2} = \dfrac{9}{25}$	$\left(\dfrac{x}{y}\right)^3 = \dfrac{x^3}{y^3}$

Place the following numbers in order, starting with the smallest number:

$$4^{\frac{1}{2}}, 4^{-2}, 2^0, 2^{-3}$$

Hence, place the numbers on a number line.

Solution

Simplify each number:

$$4^{\frac{1}{2}} = \sqrt{4} = 2$$

$$4^{-2} = \frac{1}{4^2} = \frac{1}{16} = 0.0625$$

$$2^0 = 1$$

$$2^{-3} = \frac{1}{2^3} = \frac{1}{8} = 0.125$$

> **key point**
>
> You may use a calculator to verify these answers. However, do not use the calculator only. Work **must** be shown.

Writing in order starting from smallest to largest:

$$\begin{array}{cccc} 0.0625, & 0.125, & 1, & 2, \\ 4^{-2}, & 2^{-3}, & 2^0, & 4^{\frac{1}{2}} \end{array}$$

Number line:

Simplify:

(i) $64^{\frac{3}{2}}$

(ii) $64^{\frac{2}{3}}$

Solution

(i) Method 1: $64^{\frac{3}{2}} = \sqrt[2]{64^3} = \sqrt{262\,144} = 512$

Method 2: $64^{\frac{3}{2}} = \left(\sqrt{64}\right)^3 = 8^3 = 512$

(ii) Method 1: $64^{\frac{2}{3}} = \sqrt[3]{64^2} = \sqrt[3]{4\,096} = 16$

Method 2: $64^{\frac{2}{3}} = \left(\sqrt[3]{64}\right)^2 = 4^2 = 16$

Write the following without indices.

(i) 6^{-2}

(ii) $81^{\frac{1}{2}}$

Solution

(i) $6^{-2} = \dfrac{1}{6^2} = \dfrac{1}{36}$

(ii) $81^{\frac{1}{2}} = \sqrt{81} = 9$

You could use your natural display calculator to **verify** these expressions. You can only use your calculator when the base number is a constant and not a variable. Make sure you are familiar with all the functions on your calculator.

Example

Simplify each of the following.

(i) $(a^3 \times a^4)^2$

(ii) $125^{\frac{2}{3}}$

(iii) $32^{\frac{2}{5}} - 81^{\frac{1}{4}}$

Solution

(i) $(a^3 \times a^4)^2$

$= (a^{3+4})^2$ \qquad (using the rule $a^p\, a^q = a^{p+q}$)

$= (a^7)^2$

$= a^{7 \times 2}$ \qquad (using the rule $(a^p)^q = a^{pq}$)

$= a^{14}$

(ii) $125^{\frac{2}{3}}$

$= \sqrt[3]{125^2}$ \qquad (using the rule $a^{\frac{p}{q}} = \sqrt[q]{a^p} = (\sqrt[q]{a})^p$)

$= (\sqrt[3]{125})^2$

$= 5^2$

$= 25$

(iii) $32^{\frac{2}{5}} - 81^{\frac{1}{4}}$

$\qquad = \sqrt[5]{32^2} - \sqrt[4]{81^1}$ $\qquad$ (using the rule $a^{\frac{p}{q}} = \sqrt[q]{a^p} = (\sqrt[q]{a})^p$)

$\qquad = (\sqrt[5]{32})^2 - \sqrt[4]{81}$

$\qquad = 2^2 - 3$

$\qquad = 4 - 3$

$\qquad = 1$

Example

Write $\sqrt[3]{16}$ in the form 2^k, $k \in \mathbb{Q}$.

Solution

$$\sqrt[3]{16} = \sqrt[3]{2^4} = (2^4)^{\frac{1}{3}} = 2^{\frac{4}{3}}$$

Simplify $\dfrac{2^5 \times 8^{\frac{2}{3}}}{64^{\frac{1}{2}} \times 4^2}$.

Solution

$\dfrac{2^5 \times 8^{\frac{2}{3}}}{64^{\frac{1}{2}} \times 4^2}$ $\qquad$ ($64^{\frac{1}{2}} = \sqrt{64}$ and $2^5 = 32$ and $4^2 = 16$)

$= \dfrac{32 \times \sqrt[3]{8^2}}{\sqrt{64} \times 16}$ $\qquad$ (using the rule $a^{\frac{p}{q}} = \sqrt[q]{a^p} = (\sqrt[q]{a})^p$)

$= \dfrac{32 \times \sqrt[3]{64}}{8 \times 16}$ $\qquad$ ($\sqrt{64} = 8$)

$= \dfrac{32 \times 4}{128} = \dfrac{128}{128} = 1$

Write $\dfrac{\sqrt{3} \times 27}{3^2}$ in the form of 3^n where $n \in \mathbb{Q}$.

Solution

$\dfrac{\sqrt{3} \times 27}{3^2}$

$\dfrac{3^{\frac{1}{2}} \times 3^3}{3^2}$ (since $\sqrt{3} = 3^{\frac{1}{2}}$ and $27 = 3^3$)

$\dfrac{3^{3+\frac{1}{2}}}{3^2}$ (using the rule $a^p a^q = a^{p+q}$)

$\dfrac{3^{\frac{7}{2}}}{3^2}$

$3^{\frac{7}{2}-2}$ (using the rule $\dfrac{a^p}{a^q} = a^{p-q}$)

$3^{\frac{3}{2}}$

Example

Simplify

$\dfrac{\sqrt[3]{27} \times 3}{9^{\frac{1}{2}} \times 3^4}$ into the form 3^n, where $n \in \mathbb{Z}$.

Solution

$\dfrac{\sqrt[3]{27} \times 3}{9^{\frac{1}{2}} \times 3^4}$

$\dfrac{3 \times 3}{\sqrt{9} \times 3^4}$ ($\sqrt[3]{27} = 3$ and $9^{\frac{1}{2}} = \sqrt{9}$)

$\dfrac{3^2}{3 \times 3^4}$ (using the rule $a^p a^q = a^{p+q}$)

$\dfrac{3^2}{3^5}$ (using the rule $a^p a^q = a^{p+q}$)

3^{2-5} (using the rule $\dfrac{a^p}{a^q} = a^{p-q}$)

3^{-3}

Simplify $\dfrac{x^5 \times x^2 \times \sqrt[3]{x^2}}{x^3 \times x^{\frac{4}{3}}}$, giving your answer in the form $x^{\frac{a}{b}}$, $a, b \in \mathbb{Z}$.

Solution

$\dfrac{x^5 \times x^2 \times \sqrt[3]{x^2}}{x^3 \times x^{\frac{4}{3}}}$

$\dfrac{x^5 \times x^2 \times x^{\frac{2}{3}}}{x^3 \times x^{\frac{4}{3}}}$ (use the rule $a^{\frac{p}{q}} = \sqrt[q]{a^p}$)

$\dfrac{x^{5+2+\frac{2}{3}}}{x^{3+\frac{4}{3}}}$ (use the rule $a^p a^q = a^{p+q}$)

$\dfrac{x^{\frac{23}{3}}}{x^{\frac{13}{3}}}$ (simplify powers)

$x^{\frac{23}{3} - \frac{13}{3}}$ $\left(\text{use the rule } \dfrac{a^p}{a^q} = a^{p-q}\right)$

$x^{\frac{10}{3}}$

Exponential equations

An equation involving the variable in the power is called an **exponential equation**.
Exponential equations are solved with the following steps.

1. Write all the numbers as powers of the same number (usually a prime number).
2. Write both sides as one power of the same number, using the laws of indices.
3. Equate these powers and solve this equation.

Example

Find the value of x for which $3^{x+3} = 9^x$.

Solution

$3^{x+3} = 9^x$

$3^{x+3} = (3^2)^x$ (write 9 as a base 3)

$3^{x+3} = 3^{2x}$

$x + 3 = 2x$ (equate powers)

$ 3 = 2x - x$ (subtract x from both sides)

$ 3 = x$

Find the value of x for which $25^x = 5^{2+x}$ and verify your answer.

Solution

$$25^x = 5^{2+x}$$
$$(5^2)^x = 5^{2+x} \qquad \text{(write 25 as a base 5)}$$
$$5^{2x} = 5^{2+x}$$
$$2x = 2 + x \qquad \text{(equate powers)}$$
$$2x - x = 2 \qquad \text{(subtract } x \text{ from both sides)}$$
$$x = 2$$

Verify $x = 2$ in the equation:

$$25^x = 5^{2+x}$$
$$25^2 = 5^{2+2}$$
$$25^2 = 5^4$$
$$625 = 625$$

Since the left side equals the right side, $x = 2$ satisfies the equation and so is verified as a solution.

>
>
> exam focus
>
> It is important to verify your answer in this question.

Example

Solve for x in each of the following equations:

(i) $8^{4+3x} = 32^{1+2x}$

(ii) $3^{x^2} = 27^{2x+9}$

Solution

(i)
$$8^{4+3x} = 32^{1+2x}$$
$$(2^3)^{4+3x} = (2^5)^{1+2x}$$
$$2^{12+9x} = 2^{5+10x}$$
$$12 + 9x = 5 + 10x \quad \text{(equate powers)}$$
$$7 = x$$

(ii)
$$3^{x^2} = 27^{2x+9}$$
$$3^{x^2} = (3^3)^{2x+9}$$
$$3^{x^2} = 3^{6x+27}$$
$$x^2 = 6x + 27 \quad \text{(equate powers)}$$
$$x^2 - 6x - 27 = 0$$
$$(x - 9)(x + 3) = 0$$
$$x - 9 = 0 \quad \text{or} \quad x + 3 = 0$$
$$x = 9 \quad \text{or} \quad x = -3$$

exam focus

Factorising was essential in solving this question. Factorising is a vital skill for you to have throughout your entire maths course.

Solve for x and y: $2^x = 8^{y+1}$

                 $3^{x-9} = 9^y$

Solution

$$2^x = 8^{y+1}$$
$$2^x = (2^3)^{y+1}$$
$$2^x = 2^{3y+3}$$
$$x = 3y + 3$$
$$x - 3y = 3 \qquad ①$$

$$3^{x-9} = 9^y$$
$$3^{x-9} = (3^2)^y$$
$$3^{x-9} = 3^{2y}$$
$$x - 9 = 2y$$
$$x - 2y = 9 \qquad ②$$

Use simultaneous equations to solve:

$$x - 3y = 3 \qquad ① \quad (\times -1)$$
$$\underline{x - 2y = 9 \qquad ②}$$
$$-x + 3y = -3$$
$$\underline{x - 2y = 9}$$
$$y = 6$$

Substitute $y = 6$ into ①:
$$x - 3y = 3$$
$$x - 3(6) = 3$$
$$x - 18 = 3$$
$$x = 21$$

Hence, $x = 21$ and $y = 6$

Notice the unification here between the topics of Indices and Simultaneous Equations.

Index notation

When dealing with very large or very small numbers it can be easier to perform calculations if the numbers are expressed in what is known as 'index notation' or 'scientific notation'. This means to express the numbers in the form $a \times 10^n$, where $1 \le a < 10$ and $n \in \mathbb{Z}$.

- $1\,200 = 1{\cdot}2 \times 1\,000 = 1{\cdot}2 \times 10^3$
- $35\,400\,000 = 3{\cdot}54 \times 10\,000\,000 = 3{\cdot}54 \times 10^7$
- $0{\cdot}000045 = 4{\cdot}5 \div 10\,000 = 4{\cdot}5 \times \frac{1}{10\,000} = 4{\cdot}5 \times \frac{1}{10^5} = 4{\cdot}5 \times 10^{-5}$

The natural display calculators can be very useful when working in index notation. But remember to show your steps or full marks may not be rewarded.

It is very important that you know how to put your calculator into scientific mode and be able to enter data that is in index notation.

CASIO	SHARP
Put your calculator into scientific mode:	Put your calculator into scientific mode:
SHIFT then SETUP	Set up
7 : Sci	1 : FSE
	1 : SCI

Select a number between 0 and 9. This is the number of significant figures the calculator will display. Selecting 9 will be fine.

Select a number between 0 and 9. This is the number of significant figures the calculator will display. Selecting 9 will be fine.

To enter $6 \cdot 7 \times 10^{-15}$
press the following buttons:

To enter $6 \cdot 7 \times 10^{-15}$
press the following buttons:

| 6 | · | 7 | ×10ˣ | (−) | 1 | 5 |

| 6 | · | 7 | Exp | (−) | 1 | 5 |

Example

Express $\dfrac{1 \cdot 26 \times 10^9}{2 \cdot 8 \times 10^{12}}$ in the form $a \times 10^n$,

where $1 \le a < 10$ and $n \in \mathbb{Z}$.

Solution

key point

To divide numbers in index notation, divide the numbers and subtract the powers on the 10s.

Method 1: $\dfrac{1 \cdot 26 \times 10^9}{2 \cdot 8 \times 10^{12}}$

$\dfrac{1 \cdot 26}{2 \cdot 8} \times 10^{9-12}$ (divide the numbers in the front and subtract the powers of the 10)

$0 \cdot 45 \times 10^{-3}$

$4 \cdot 5 \times 10^{-4}$ (multiply the $0 \cdot 45$ by 10 and divide the 10^{-3} by 10)

Method 2: Start by putting your calculator into scientific mode.

$$\dfrac{1 \cdot 26 \times 10^9}{2 \cdot 8 \times 10^{12}} = 4 \cdot 5 \times 10^{-4}$$

Express 2^{24} in the form $a \times 10^n$, where $1 \leq a < 10$ and $n \in \mathbb{N}$, correct to three significant figures.

Solution

Method 1: Use your calculator to find the value of 2^{24}.

$2^{24} = 16\ 777\ 216$ (on calculator display)

$2^{24} = 1 \cdot 6777216 \times 10\ 000\ 000$

$2^{24} = 1 \cdot 6777216 \times 10^7$

$2^{24} = 1 \cdot 6800000 \times 10^7$ (to three significant figures)

$2^{24} = 1 \cdot 68 \times 10^7$

Method 2: Put your calculator into scientific mode. Enter 2^{24} and press the equal button:

$1 \cdot 6777216 \times 10^7$ (on calculator display)

$1 \cdot 6800000 \times 10^7$ (to three significant figures)

$1 \cdot 68 \times 10^7$

Example

Simplify $\dfrac{(2 \cdot 4 \times 10^{13}) \times (1 \cdot 8 \times 10^{-4})}{3 \cdot 5 \times 10^3}$.

Solution

Start by putting your calculator into scientific mode.

> **key point**
>
> To multiply numbers in index notation, multiply the numbers and add the powers on the 10s.

$\dfrac{(2 \cdot 4 \times 10^{13}) \times (1 \cdot 8 \times 10^{-4})}{3 \cdot 5 \times 10^3}$

$= \dfrac{4 \cdot 32 \times 10^9}{3 \cdot 5 \times 10^3}$ (use your calculator to simplify the top)

$= 1 \cdot 23428571 \times 10^6$ (use your calculator to simplify the fraction)

The diameters of Venus and Saturn are 1.21×10^4 km and 1.21×10^5 km. What is the difference between the diameters of the two planets? Give your answer in the form of $a \times 10^n$, where $n \in \mathbb{Z}$ and $1 \leq a < 10$.

Solution

Start by putting your calculator into scientific mode.

Difference in diameters = Diameter of Saturn − Diameter of Venus

Difference in diameters = $1.21 \times 10^5 - 1.21 \times 10^4$

Difference in diameters = 1.089×10^5 km

Given that $x = 2 \times 10^{-3}$ and $y = 7 \times 10^{-4}$, evaluate $x + 8y$.

Express your answer in the form $a \times 10^n$, where $n \in \mathbb{Z}$ and $1 \leq a < 10$.

Solution

Start by putting your calculator into scientific mode.

$$x + 8y$$
$$(2 \times 10^{-3}) + 8(7 \times 10^{-4})$$
$$2 \times 10^{-3} + 5.6 \times 10^{-3}$$
$$7.6 \times 10^{-3}$$

One atom of carbon is found to have a mass of $1·994 \times 10^{-23}$ grams.

(i) Find the mass of 1 250 000 atoms of carbon.

(ii) A sample of carbon is made up of purely carbon atoms. Find the number of carbon atoms, to the nearest whole number, within a carbon sample that has a mass of 8 kg.

Answer in the form $a \times 10^n$, where $1 \leq a < 10$ and $n \in \mathbb{Z}$ where a is to the nearest whole number.

Solution

(i)
$$1 \text{ carbon atom} = 1·994 \times 10^{-23}$$
$$1 \text{ 250 000 carbon atoms} = (1 \text{ 250 000})(1·994 \times 10^{-23})$$
$$= 2·4925 \times 10^{-17} \text{ grams}$$

(ii) 8 kg = 8 000 g

$$\text{Number of atoms} = \frac{\text{Total mass}}{\text{Mass of one atom}}$$

$$= \frac{8 \text{ 000}}{1·994 \times 10^{-23}}$$

$$= 4·012 \times 10^{26}$$

Therefore, the sample contains 4×10^{26} carbon atoms.

Irrational numbers (surds)

An irrational number is a number which cannot be written in the form $\dfrac{a}{b}$, where a and b are integers.

This means an irrational number cannot be expressed as a fraction where the numerator and the denominator are whole numbers.

Irrational numbers were also covered in Chapter 1.

Properties of surds:

1. $\sqrt{ab} = \sqrt{a}\sqrt{b}$

2. $\sqrt{\dfrac{a}{b}} = \dfrac{\sqrt{a}}{\sqrt{b}}$

3. $\sqrt{a}\sqrt{a} = a$

Simplification of surds

Find the largest possible perfect square number greater than 1 that will divide evenly into the number under the square root.

Then use the property $\sqrt{ab} = \sqrt{a}\sqrt{b}$.

Remember: perfect squares are 1, 4, 9, 16, 25, 36, 49, . . .

Example

Express each of the following in its simplest surd form:

(i) $\sqrt{27}$ (ii) $\dfrac{1}{2}\sqrt{72}$ (iii) $\sqrt{2\dfrac{1}{4}}$

Solution

(i) $\sqrt{27} = \sqrt{9 \times 3} = \sqrt{9}\sqrt{3} = 3\sqrt{3}$

(ii) $\dfrac{1}{2}\sqrt{72} = \dfrac{1}{2}\sqrt{36 \times 2} = \dfrac{1}{2}\sqrt{36}\sqrt{2} = \dfrac{1}{2}(6)\sqrt{2} = 3\sqrt{2}$

(iii) $\sqrt{2\dfrac{1}{4}} = \sqrt{\dfrac{9}{4}} = \dfrac{\sqrt{9}}{\sqrt{4}} = \dfrac{3}{2}$

The natural display calculators can be very useful when **verifying** answers to questions on surds. Remember, marks may be lost for not showing your workings.

Addition and subtraction

Adding and subtracting surds uses the same method as when adding and subtracting terms in algebra.

Surds can be added or subtracted *only* when they have the same irrational parts. If the irrational parts are not the same, reduce each surd to its simplest form, where possible.

Example

Express $\sqrt{72} - \sqrt{8}$ in the form $k\sqrt{2}$, where $k \in \mathbb{N}$.

Solution

$\sqrt{72} - \sqrt{8}$

$= \sqrt{36}\sqrt{2} - \sqrt{4}\sqrt{2}$

$= 6\sqrt{2} - 2\sqrt{2}$

$= 4\sqrt{2}$

key point

Addition and subtraction

Only like surds can be added or subtracted. Express each surd in its simplest form and add or subtract like surds.

exam Q

Use the properties of surds to show that $\sqrt{98} - \sqrt{18} + \sqrt{2}$ simplifies to $5\sqrt{2}$.

Solution

$\sqrt{98} - \sqrt{18} + \sqrt{2}$

$= \sqrt{49}\sqrt{2} - \sqrt{9}\sqrt{2} + \sqrt{2}$

$= 7\sqrt{2} - 3\sqrt{2} + \sqrt{2}$

$= 4\sqrt{2} + \sqrt{2}$

$= 5\sqrt{2}$

exam focus

This exam question was not well answered by candidates.

Multiplication

Multiplication of surds uses the same method as when multiplying terms in algebra. When multiplying surds, multiply the rational parts by the rational parts and the irrational parts by the irrational parts.

Example

Express the following in its simplest surd form: $3\sqrt{5} \times 2\sqrt{3}$.

Solution

$3\sqrt{5} \times 2\sqrt{3}$

$= (3 \times 2) \times (\sqrt{5} \times \sqrt{3})$ (Rational parts are 3 and 2. Irrational parts are $\sqrt{5}$ and $\sqrt{3}$.)

$= 6\sqrt{15}$

Example

Express the following in its simplest surd form: $2\sqrt{5}(3 + 4\sqrt{5})$.

Solution

$2\sqrt{5}(3 + 4\sqrt{5})$

$6\sqrt{5} + 8\sqrt{25}$

$6\sqrt{5} + 8(5)$

$6\sqrt{5} + 40$

Remember:
$(\sqrt{a})^2 = \sqrt{a} \times \sqrt{a} = a$

Given that $(\sqrt{d})^2 = d$, multiply out and simplify $(c + \sqrt{d})^2$.

Solution

$(c + \sqrt{d})^2$

$(c + \sqrt{d})(c + \sqrt{d})$

$c^2 + c\sqrt{d} + c\sqrt{d} + d$ since $(\sqrt{d})^2 = d$

$c^2 + 2c\sqrt{d} + d$

Simplify $\sqrt{3}(2\sqrt{6} - 4\sqrt{3}) - \sqrt{10}(3\sqrt{5} - 2\sqrt{10})$ without the use of a calculator.

Express your answer in the form $a + b\sqrt{2}$, where $a, b \in \mathbb{Z}$.

Solution

$\sqrt{3}(2\sqrt{6} - 4\sqrt{3}) - \sqrt{10}(3\sqrt{5} - 2\sqrt{10})$

$2\sqrt{18} - 4\sqrt{9} - 3\sqrt{50} + 2\sqrt{100}$

$2\sqrt{9}\sqrt{2} - 4(3) - 3\sqrt{25}\sqrt{2} + 2(10)$

$2(3)\sqrt{2} - 12 - 3(5)\sqrt{2} + 20$

$6\sqrt{2} - 15\sqrt{2} + 8$

$-9\sqrt{2} + 8$

$8 - 9\sqrt{2}$

Express the following in simplest surd form: $(2 + 3\sqrt{5})(4 - \sqrt{5})$.

Solution

$(2 + 3\sqrt{5})(4 - \sqrt{5})$

$2(4 - \sqrt{5}) + 3\sqrt{5}(4 - \sqrt{5})$ (use distributive law)

$8 - 2\sqrt{5} + 12\sqrt{5} - 3(5)$ (multiply out brackets)

$8 + 10\sqrt{5} - 15$ (simplify)

$-7 + 10\sqrt{5}$

Remember the distributive law:

$(A + B)(C + D) = A(C + D) + B(C + D)$

Simplify $\left(\sqrt{12} + \dfrac{1}{\sqrt{12}}\right)\left(\sqrt{12} - \dfrac{1}{\sqrt{12}}\right)$ without the use of a calculator.

Express your answer in the form $\dfrac{a}{b}$, where $a, b \in \mathbb{N}$.

Solution

$\left(\sqrt{12} + \dfrac{1}{\sqrt{12}}\right)\left(\sqrt{12} - \dfrac{1}{\sqrt{12}}\right)$

$\sqrt{12}\left(\sqrt{12} - \dfrac{1}{\sqrt{12}}\right) + \dfrac{1}{\sqrt{12}}\left(\sqrt{12} - \dfrac{1}{\sqrt{12}}\right)$

$\sqrt{144} - \dfrac{\sqrt{12}}{\sqrt{12}} + \dfrac{\sqrt{12}}{\sqrt{12}} - \dfrac{1}{\sqrt{144}}$

$12 - 1 + 1 - \dfrac{1}{12}$

$12 - \dfrac{1}{12}$

$\dfrac{143}{12}$ (note: you must leave the answer in the form $\frac{a}{b}$, as per instructed in the question)

Show that $(2 + \sqrt{7})(2 - \sqrt{7})$ is rational.

Solution

$(2 + \sqrt{7})(2 - \sqrt{7})$

$2(2 - \sqrt{7}) + \sqrt{7}(2 - \sqrt{7})$ (use distributive law)

$4 - 2\sqrt{7} + 2\sqrt{7} - \sqrt{7}(\sqrt{7})$ (multiply out brackets)

$4 - 7$ (note: $(\sqrt{7})(\sqrt{7}) = 7$)

-3

Since there are no surds in the answer, it is rational.

Therefore, $(2 + \sqrt{7})(2 - \sqrt{7})$ is rational.

key point

Rational means not irrational, that is, that there are no surds.

x and $\sqrt{x^2}$ are **not** always equal.

Give an example of a value of x, and the corresponding value of $\sqrt{x^2}$, which are **not** equal.

Solution

Let $x = -2$

Then the value of $\sqrt{x^2} = \sqrt{(-2)^2}$

$\qquad\qquad\qquad = \sqrt{4}$

$\qquad\qquad\qquad = 2$

So $x \neq \sqrt{x^2}$ in this case.

For any negative value of x, $x \neq \sqrt{x^2}$

- [ ] To recognise a repeating pattern and to make predictions from that pattern.
- [ ] To represent patterns with tables, diagrams and graphs.
- [ ] To generate and write expressions/formulae from patterns for particular terms in a sequence.
- [ ] To know about linear, quadratic and exponential patterns.
- [ ] To understand and be able to carry out the operation called differencing (change).

An introduction to pattern

A pattern always has a logical sequence.

Examples of pattern in everyday life:

1. Traffic lights: Green, amber, red, green, amber, ...
2. Tidal movements: high tide, low tide, high tide, low tide, ...

Sequences

A sequence is a particular order in which related things follow each other. For example:

(i) 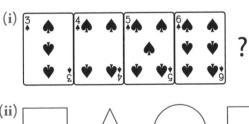 ?

(ii)  ?

(iii)  ?

(iv) 1, 3, 6, 10, ?

- The first term of a sequence is called T_1, the second term is T_2 and so on.
- To predict what will come next in a sequence, we must find a rule that links one number or diagram with the next.

In our course we study three main types of numeric sequences and their associated graphs.

1. **Linear sequences, e.g. 2, 5, 8, 11, 14, ...**

   A linear (arithmetic) sequence is formed by adding/subtracting the same amount to any term to get the next term. This 'same amount' is usually called the **common difference.**

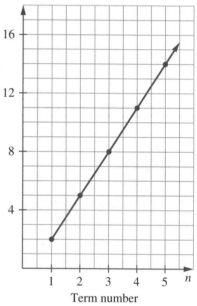

2. **Quadratic sequences, e.g. 0, 5, 8, 9, 8, 5, 0**

   Sequences that have an nth term containing n^2 as the highest power are called quadratic sequences. We use a technique called differencing, explained later in this chapter, when working with quadratic sequences.

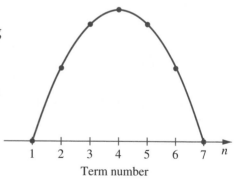

3. Exponential sequences, e.g. 2, 4, 8, 16 . . .

In these sequences, when we look for a term to term rule, we find that it involves multiplying (by 2 in this case). When terms are calculated by multiplying, the sequence is always exponential.

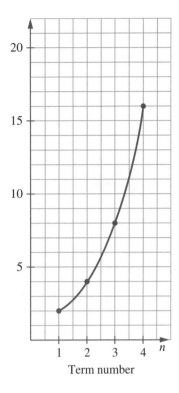

Term number

Predicting the pattern

Much of mathematics is about pattern. The following questions are simple and numeric.

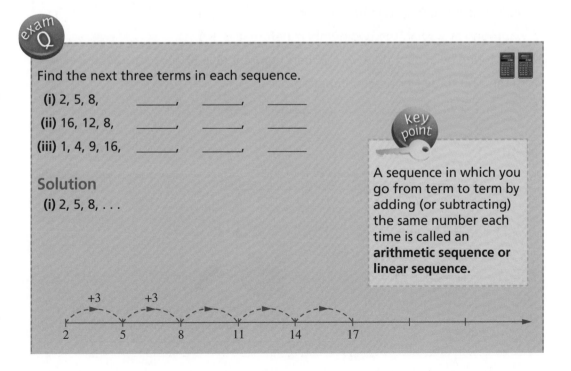

exam Q

Find the next three terms in each sequence.

(i) 2, 5, 8, _____, _____, _____

(ii) 16, 12, 8, _____, _____, _____

(iii) 1, 4, 9, 16, _____, _____, _____

key point

A sequence in which you go from term to term by adding (or subtracting) the same number each time is called an **arithmetic sequence or linear sequence.**

Solution

(i) 2, 5, 8, . . .

(ii) 16, 12, 8, . . .

(iii) 1, 4, 9, 16, . . .

key point

A much tougher question. This is not an arithmetic sequence. Some outside-the-box thinking makes the solution simple. It is in fact a quadratic sequence.

$(1)^2$, $(2)^2$, $(3)^2$, $(4)^2$, $(5)^2$, $(6)^2$, $(7)^2$

1,   4,   9,   16,   25,   36,   49

The first eight Fibonacci numbers are 0, 1, 1, 2, 3, 5, 8, 13.

Fibonacci numbers are found by adding the previous two numbers to get the next one.

5 was found by adding the two numbers before it (2 + 3).

8 was found by adding the two numbers before it (3 + 5).

13 was found by adding the two numbers before it (5 + 8).

Find the next three Fibonacci numbers:

0, 1, 1, 2, 3, 5, 8, 13, _____, _____, _____.

Solution

| 0 | 1 | 1 | 2 | 3 | 5 | 8 | 13 | | | |
| T_1 | T_2 | T_3 | T_4 | T_5 | T_6 | T_7 | T_8 | T_9 | T_{10} | T_{11} |

$T_9 = T_8 + T_7 = 13 + 8 = 21$

$T_{10} = T_9 + T_8 = 21 + 13 = 34$

$T_{11} = T_{10} + T_9 = 34 + 21 = 55$

exam focus

Some questions on pattern are neither linear, quadratic nor exponential.

In a number pyramid you add the two numbers in the lower blocks to find the number in the block above (for example, 2 + 3 = 5).

Complete the number pyramid by filling in the empty spaces.

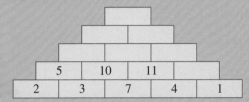

Solution

First

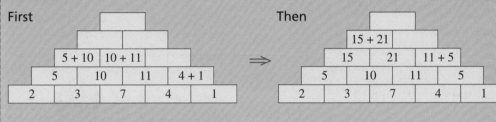

⟹

Then

Finally

Example

Row 3									
Row 4		1	4	6	4	1			
Row 5	1	5	10	10	5	1			
Row 6	1	6	15	20	15	6	1		
Row 7									

The pattern indicated above shows row 4, row 5 and row 6 of Pascal's triangle.

Write down the pattern for **(i)** row 3 **(ii)** row 7.

Solution

(i) Row 3   1   3   3   1

     Row 4   1   4   6   4   1

     Row 5   1   5   10   10   5   1

     Row 6   1   6   15   20   15   6   1

(ii) Row 7   1   7   21   35   35   21   7   1

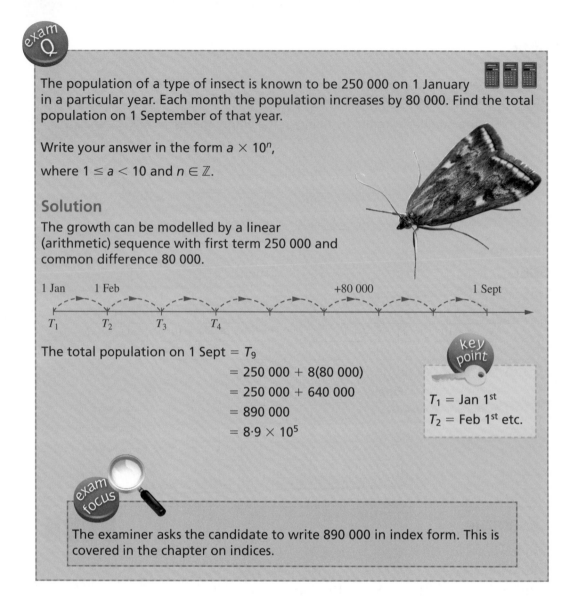

The population of a type of insect is known to be 250 000 on 1 January in a particular year. Each month the population increases by 80 000. Find the total population on 1 September of that year.

Write your answer in the form $a \times 10^n$,

where $1 \le a < 10$ and $n \in \mathbb{Z}$.

Solution

The growth can be modelled by a linear (arithmetic) sequence with first term 250 000 and common difference 80 000.

The total population on 1 Sept $= T_9$

$$= 250\ 000 + 8(80\ 000)$$
$$= 250\ 000 + 640\ 000$$
$$= 890\ 000$$
$$= 8{\cdot}9 \times 10^5$$

key point

$T_1 = $ Jan 1st
$T_2 = $ Feb 1st etc.

exam focus

The examiner asks the candidate to write 890 000 in index form. This is covered in the chapter on indices.

Predicting pattern from given graphs and diagrams

Not all patterns are numeric. For example, look at a series of shapes made using matches.

How many matches will be needed for the 6th shape?

Answer: 5, 9, 13, 17, 21 then 25 matches for the 6th shape

Three experiments on temperature are done in the science lab. Pupils record and plot the temperature of each experiment each hour, for 5 hours.

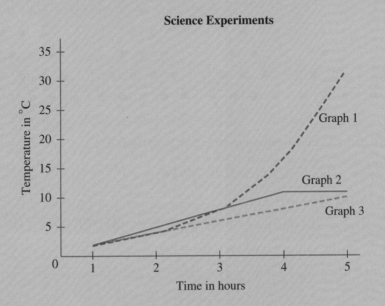

Science Experiments

In experiment A, the temperature doubles every hour.

In experiment B, the temperature increases by 2° every hour.

In experiment C, the temperature increases by 3° each hour for three hours and then remains constant.

Identify each experiment by its number on the graph.

Solution

In experiment B the temperature increases by +2° every hour. This is what we call a linear (straight line) sequence.

B is associated with Graph 3.

Experiment C is also linear but stops increasing after three seconds where the graph flattens.

Hence, C is associated with Graph 2.

By elimination, A is associated with Graph 1.

key point

Graph 1 is exponential.

Example

In the following pattern, the first figure represents one dot, the second represents three dots, etc.

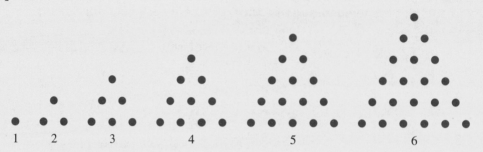

This pattern can also be described in function notation:

$f(1) = 1,$ $f(2) = 3,$ $f(3) = 6,$ etc.

(i) Hence or otherwise, write down:

    (a) $f(4)$ (b) $f(6)$ (c) $f(7)$ (d) $f(8)$

(ii) Write down the value of q where $f(q) = 55$.

(iii) Solve for x when $f(x) + f(x + 1) = 64$.

Solution

(i) From the diagram, we construct the following table.

Figure	1	2	3	4	5	6	7	8	9	10
Number of dots	1	3	6	10	15	21	28	36	45	55

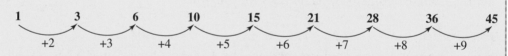

    (a) $f(4) = 10$ (b) $f(6) = 21$ (c) $f(7) = 28$ (d) $f(8) = 36$

(ii) By observation from the table constructed in part (i):

$$f(10) = 55 \quad \text{which means} \quad q = 10$$

(iii) $f(x) + f(x + 1)$ represent two consecutive figures.

We write the sequence 1, 3, 6, 10, 15, 21, 28, 36, 45, . . . and by trial and improvement find $28 + 36 = 64$.

$\Rightarrow \quad f(7) + f(8) = 64$

$\Rightarrow \quad f(x) + f(x + 1) = 64$ Answer: $x = 7$

Melissa bought a horse in 2007 for €500. She took the horse to the sales each year for three years to have it valued but did not sell. She recorded the values on the graph below.

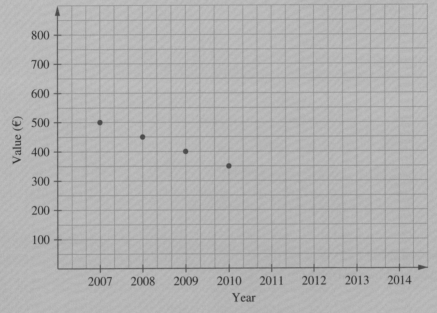

(i) Use a line to join the points on the graph.

(ii) If the pattern continued, what was the horse worth in 2011?

(iii) How much does the horse lose in value each year?

(iv) Melissa will sell the horse when it reaches a value of €200. If the pattern continues, in what year will she sell the horse?

(v) James bought a horse for €700 in 2007. His horse loses value at a constant rate. It was worth €100 in 2011. Mark these two points on the graph above and join them with a straight line.

(vi) In what year will the two horses have the same value? What is that value?

(vii) Louise examines the graph and says, 'Looking at the slopes of the lines, I can tell which horse loses value faster.' Explain in your own words what Louise means.

This question links Pattern and Coordinate Geometry. The examiner will often create this type of link.

Solution

(i)

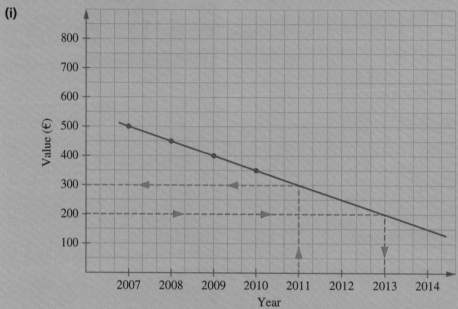

(ii) €300 (reading from the graph ---▶---)

(iii) −€50 in value each year, by observation from the graph

(iv) 2013 (reading from the graph ---▶---)

(v)

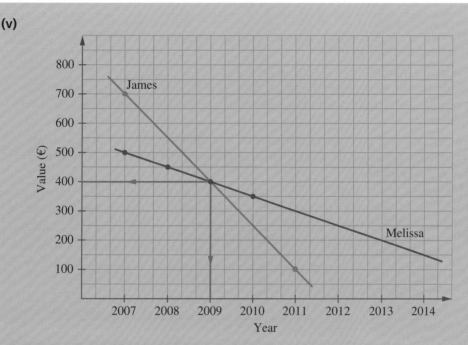

(vi) Reading from the graph above, the two horses have the same value in 2009 and that value was €400.

(vii) The (downward) slope of Melissa's line tells Louise the value of Melissa's horse is decreasing. However, the much steeper (downward) slope of James's line tells Louise the value of his horse is decreasing faster.

The point of intersection of the two lines gives the answers to part **(vi)**.

The diagram shows the percentage of their total sleep that men and women spend in deep sleep, depending on their age in years, *A*.

(i) Gina is a 20-year-old woman. Use the diagram to estimate the percentage of her total sleep that Gina spends in deep sleep. Show your work on the graph.

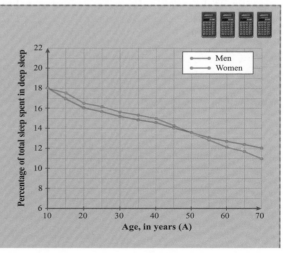

(ii) Gina sleeps an average of 8 hours in total each night. Work out how many hours Gina spends in deep sleep on average each week (7 nights).

(iii) Fill in the inequality in A to show the age range for which women spend a lower percentage of their sleep in deep sleep than men do.

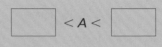

(iv) The data in the survey was collected from 6 billion nights of sleep, where a billion is a thousand million. Write 6 billion in the form $a \times 10^n$, where $1 \leq a < 10$ and $n \in \mathbb{N}$.

(v) Phillippe uses a linear model to estimate the percentage of their total sleep that men spend in deep sleep, from 42 to 66 years of age. Some of his results are in the table below. Complete the table below so that the percentages follow a linear pattern. Show your working out.

Age, A (years)	40	45	50	55	60
Percentage of Total Sleep spent in Deep Sleep	15·0		13·6		12·2

(vi) Using the values in the table above, Phillippe writes the percentage of sleep spent in deep sleep as a function of age, A, for $40 \leq A \leq 60$. The graph of this function is a line with a slope of -0.14. Explain what -0.14 means in the context of this question.

Solution

(i) Gina is 20 years old, so we go to 20 on the horizontal axis. She is a woman so we look at the red graph, which shows that an age of 20 corresponds to a percentage of 16% for a woman. Therefore, we estimate Gina spends 16% of her total sleep in a deep sleep.

(ii) Gina is in a deep sleep for 16% of 8 hours per night = 1·28 hours of deep sleep per night
For one week (7 nights), total hours of deep sleep = 1·28 × 7 = 8·96 hours

(iii) Women spend a lower percentage of their sleep in deep sleep than men do in the region on the graph where the red graph is lower down than the blue graph. This occurs between the ages of 10 years and 50 years. Completing the inequality:

$$\boxed{10} < A < \boxed{50}$$

(iv) 6 billion = 6 × 1000 × 1000000
= 6 000 000 000
= 6×10^9

(v) A linear pattern means that the difference between each of the terms is the same. Between the ages of 40 and 50 the percentage changes from 15·0% to 13·6% which is a decrease of 1·4%. Since it is a linear pattern, the change between the ages of 40 and 45 is a decrease of 0·7, half of the change between 40 and 50 years.

Apply this first difference of −0·7 to find the missing values in the table:

Age, A (years)	40	45	50	55	60
Percentage of Total Sleep spent in Deep Sleep	15·0	14·3	13·6	12·9	12·2

−0·7   −0·7   −0·7   −0·7

(vi) Slope $= -0·14 = \dfrac{-0.14}{1} = \dfrac{\text{Rise}}{\text{Run}}$

This means that for every 1 year increase in age (the run), there is a decrease of 0·14% in the time spent in deep sleep (the rise).

Differencing (change)

Many investigative and problem-solving questions lead to a sequence of numbers. The technique of differencing is useful in certain situations involving sequences. To observe an application of differencing, we apply the technique to the sequence 3, 7, 13, 21, 31, 43 . . .

To find the first difference:

- Subtract the first number in the sequence from the second.
- Subtract the second number in the sequence from the third.
- Subtract the third number in the sequence from the fourth and so on.

The second differences can be found by taking the difference of the first differences. The third differences can then be found and so on again.

Hence we find:

	First difference (first change)	Second difference (change of change)	Third difference (change of change of change)
$T_1 = 3$			
	4		
$T_2 = 7$		2	
	6		0
$T_3 = 13$		2	
	8		0
$T_4 = 21$		2	
	10		0
$T_5 = 31$		2	
	12		
$T_6 = 43$			

key point

- When the first difference is the same value each time, the pattern is referred to as a linear pattern. When graphed this will be a straight line.
- When the second difference is the same value each time, the pattern is referred to as a quadratic pattern. When graphed this will be a curve.

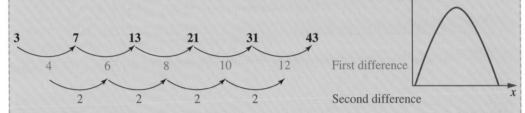

If the second difference is not constant, the pattern is **not** quadratic.

Example

A stone is dropped from the top of a building and lands on the ground below. The total distance that it fell from the top of the building was recorded at 1 second intervals. It landed on the ground after 5 seconds.

The results are shown in the table.

Time (seconds)	Distance (metres)
0	0
1	6
2	24
3	54
4	96
5	150

(i) What is the height of the building?

(ii) Do these results form a linear relationship? Explain your answer.

(iii) Could these results be represented by a quadratic function? Explain your answer.

Solution

(i) Since it takes the stone 5 seconds to fall 150 m, the height is 150 m.

(ii) and (iii)

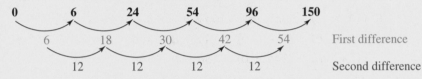

0   6   24   54   96   150

6   18   30   42   54   First difference

12   12   12   12   Second difference

Not linear, as the first differences are not constant. However, since the second difference is constant, it is quadratic.

exam Q

Investigate whether the pattern in the table below is linear, quadratic or exponential. Explain your conclusion.

Term 1	Term 2	Term 3	Term 4	Term 5
$2a - b + 2c$	$8a - 2b + 2c$	$18a - 3b + 2c$	$32a - 4b + 2c$	$50a - 5b + 2c$

Solution

Term 2 − Term 1 = $(8a - 2b + 2c) - (2a - b + 2c)$
$$= 8a - 2b + 2c - 2a + b - 2c$$
$$= 6a - b$$

Term 3 − Term 2 = $(18a - 3b + 2c) - (8a - 2b + 2c)$
$$= 18a - 3b + 2c - 8a + 2b - 2c$$
$$= 10a - b$$

Term 4 − Term 3 = $(32a - 4b + 2c) - (18a - 3b + 2c)$
$$= 32a - 4b + 2c - 18a + 3b - 2c$$
$$= 14a - b$$

Term 5 − Term 4 = $(50a - 5b + 2c) - (32a - 4b + 2c)$
$$= 50a - 5b + 2c - 32a + 4b - 2c$$
$$= 18a - b$$

Term 1	Term 2	Term 3	Term 4	Term 5
$2a - b + 2c$	$8a - 2b + 2c$	$18a - 3b + 2c$	$32a - 4b + 2c$	$50a - 5b + 2c$

$6a - b$ $10a - b$ $14a - b$ $18a - b$ First difference

$4a$ $4a$ $4a$ Second difference

key point

For the second difference we write:

$(10a - b) - (6a - b) = 10a - b - 6a + b = 4a$

$(14a - b) - (10a - b) = 14a - b - 10a + b = 4a$

$(18a - b) - (14a - b) = 18a - b - 14a + b = 4a$

Also notice the link with Subtraction in Algebra.

Finally, since the second difference is constant, the relationship is quadratic.

exam focus

This question was awarded 15 marks for a totally correct solution.

0 marks for no correct work.

7 marks awarded for **one** correct first difference.

12 marks awarded for all differences correct but with no conclusion or an incorrect conclusion. There were no other possible scores, i.e. only 0, 7, 12, 15 marks.

exam Q

(i) Only one linear pattern begins with '1, 7'.
Fill in the three boxes below so that the numbers form this **linear** pattern.

Linear pattern: 1,   7,   ☐ , ☐ , ☐

(ii) Many different quadratic patterns begin with '1, 7'.
Fill in the three boxes below so that the numbers form a **quadratic** pattern

Quadratic pattern: 1,   7,   ☐ , ☐ , ☐

Solution

(i) In a linear pattern, the first difference is the same in each case.
The first difference going from 1 to 7 is + 6.
Continue the pattern by adding 6 to each term:

Linear pattern: 1,   7, | 13 | , | 19 | , | 25 |

+6   +6   +6   +6   First Difference

(ii) In a quadratic pattern, the second difference is the same in each case.
The first difference going from 1 to 7 is + 6.
We can pick a second difference. There are an infinite number of possibilities.
We will make the second difference equal to +2.
This will give a pattern as follows:

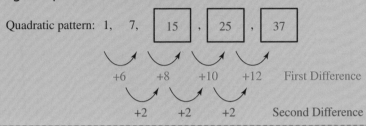

Quadratic pattern: 1, 7, 15 , 25 , 37

+6   +8   +10   +12   First Difference

+2   +2   +2   Second Difference

Orla is asked to write down a **quadratic** sequence. She writes down the following:

5,   6,   9,   14,   22,   30,   41

Exactly one of the terms in Orla's sequence is incorrect.
Write down the correct quadratic sequence in the spaces below.
You may only change **one** of the terms in Orla's sequence.

Solution

Investigate the first and second differences:

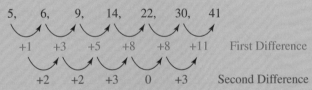

5,   6,   9,   14,   22,   30,   41

+1   +3   +5   +8   +8   +11   First Difference

+2   +2   +3   0   +3   Second Difference

We can see that the first two second differences are the same, but then it is no longer consistent.

So, we need to make all of the second differences +2 and then adjust the first differences and the original sequence accordingly:

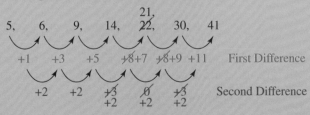

 21,
5,   6,   9,   14,   2̶2̶,   30,   41

+1   +3   +5   ̶+̶8̶+7   ̶+̶8̶+9   +11   First Difference

+2   +2   ̶+̶3̶+2   ̶0̶+2   ̶+̶3̶+2   Second Difference

We can see that changing the 22 to a 21 will correct Orla's sequence to make it quadratic.

Exponential sequences

The syllabus restricts our study of exponential sequences to two types: doubling and trebling. Below is an example and a graph of each type.

Type 1   Doubling   **Type 2**   Trebling

         6, 12, 24, 48, 96 . . .   2, 6, 18, 54, 162 . . .

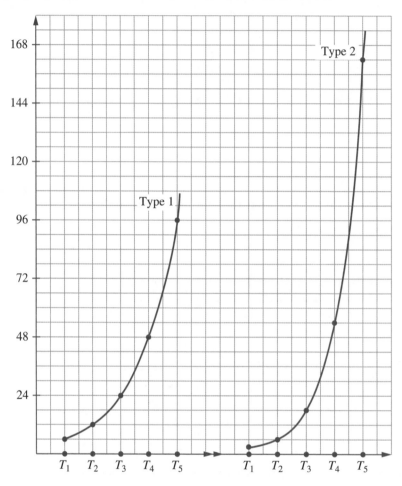

Exponent is another word for power, e.g. 3^1, 3^2, 3^3, 3^4, . . . In everyday language, exponential growth is used to indicate very rapid growth. Remember:

$$\text{Exponent} = \text{Power} = \text{Index}$$

Given the right conditions of food, moisture and warmth, some bacteria can divide into two every 5 minutes. This is known as binary fission and is especially important in the food industry in order to avoid food poisoning. The diagram below shows the growth by division of one bacterium.

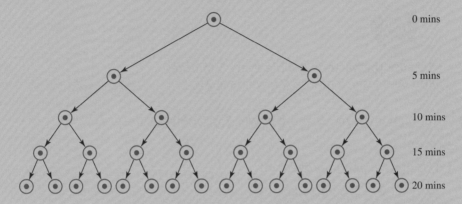

0 mins

5 mins

10 mins

15 mins

20 mins

(i) How many bacteria will this single one have become after multiplying for

(a) 30 minutes   **(b)** 60 minutes?

(ii) Complete this table.

Time in minutes	0	5	10	15	20	25	30	35	40
Number of bacteria	2^0	2^1			2^4				

(iii) Use the table of results from part **(ii)** to write down a formula for the number of bacteria after 1 hour.

(iv) Hence or otherwise, write down a formula for the number of bacteria after n minutes.

(v) Elaina lays out a buffet meal some time before her guests are to eat it. If the buffet is left in good bacteria breeding conditions:

(a) How long will it take for one bacteria to multiply to become over 1 000 000?

(b) Starting with one bacteria, how many bacteria will there be if the buffet is left for 2·5 hours? Give your answer to the nearest billion bacteria.

Solution

(i) The pattern is 1, 2, 4, 8, 16, 32, 64, 128, 256, 512, 1 026, 2 048, . . .

Hence **(a)** after 30 minutes there are 64 bacteria and **(b)** after 60 minutes there are 4 096 bacteria.

(ii)

Time in minutes	0	5	10	15	20	25	30	35	40
Number of bacteria	2^0	2^1	2^2	2^3	2^4	2^5	2^6	2^7	2^8

(iii) After 1 hour = After 60 minutes = 2^{12} (= 4 096).

> Because the bacteria double every 5 minutes
> and 60 mins ÷ 5 mins = 12, we have 2^{12}.

(iv) After *n* minutes, $n \div 5$ = the power 2 is raised by.

Answer: $2^{\frac{n}{5}}$

(v) (a) Using trial and improvement:

$2^{20} = 1\ 048\ 576$ bacteria

$2^{19} = 524\ 228$ bacteria

Hence $20 = \frac{n}{5}$

$100 = n$

That is, 100 minutes = 1 hour 40 minutes.

(b) 2·5 hours = $2\frac{1}{2}$ hours = 150 minutes

Then $2 = \frac{n}{5}$ becomes $2^{\frac{150}{5}} = 2^{30} = 1\ 073\ 741\ 824$

Answer: 1 000 000 000 = 1 billion bacteria

- ☐ To be familiar with set symbols and set notation.
- ☐ To be able to construct and interpret Venn diagrams.
- ☐ To know the meaning of terms such as subsets, cardinal number, set difference and complement of a set.
- ☐ To be able to identify whether the commutative, associative or distributive properties hold in situations involving sets.
- ☐ To gain the necessary skills to solve problems concerning two or sometimes three sets.
- ☐ To be able to apply sets in the many different topics where it may be examined, e.g. probability, simultaneous equations, number theory.

Basic revision of sets terminology

1. **A set is a well-defined collection of objects**

   The set of whole numbers between $2\frac{1}{4}$ and $5\frac{1}{3}$ is a well-defined set, but the set of good actors is not. Different people will give different answers.

2. **Equal sets**

   Two sets are equal if they contain exactly the same elements.

   If $E = \{1, 3, 8, 9\}$ and $F = \{9, 3, 1, 8\}$ then $E = F$.

3. **Element of a set**

   If $E = \{$The first five letters in the alphabet$\}$ then:

   (i) d is an element of E and is written as $d \in E$.

   (ii) y is not an element of E and is written as $y \notin E$.

4. **The universal set (U)**

   The set from which all other sets are being considered is called the universal set, U.

5. If every element of a set E is also an element of a set F, then E is said to be a subset of F. This is written $E \subset F$.

6. Union of two sets $(E \cup F)$

   The union of two sets is found by putting together, in a new set, all the elements of E and F without repeating an element. It is written $E \cup F$.

   If $E = \{b, p, q, y\}$ and $F = \{a, b, c, y\}$, then $E \cup F = \{a, b, c, p, q, y\}$.

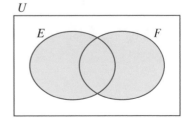

When listing the elements of a set, place the elements between chain brackets { } and separate them with commas. An element is never repeated and the order of the elements is **not** important.

7. Intersection of two sets $(E \cap F)$

   The intersection of two sets E and F is the set of elements that are in **both** E and F.

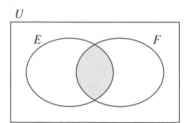

8. The complement of a set (E')

   The complement of a set E is the set of elements in the universal set U which are not in E.

   It is written as E'.

   The booklet of formulae and tables (approved for use in the state examinations) has some of the set symbols.

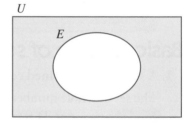

exam Q

The Venn diagram represents the sets

The diagram represents the sets:

Natural numbers $\mathbb{N}$

Integers $\mathbb{Z}$

Rational numbers $\mathbb{Q}$

Real numbers $\mathbb{R}$

Insert each of the following numbers in the correct place on the diagram:

$(-2)^3$, 0, $-\dfrac{1}{4}$, 4^{-1}, $3^{\frac{1}{2}}$, $(-5)^2$ and $27^{\frac{1}{3}}$

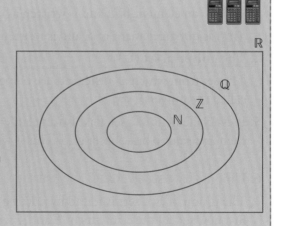

Solution

By using your calculator or otherwise:

$(-2)^3 = -2 \times -2 \times 2 = -8$ Integer

$4^{-1} = \frac{1}{4} = 0.25$ Rational

$3^{\frac{1}{2}} = \sqrt{3} = 1 \cdot 732050808 \cdots \cdots$ Real

$(27)^{\frac{1}{3}} = 3$ Natural Number

0 Integer number

$-\frac{1}{4}$ Rational

$(-5)^2 = -5 \times -5 = 25$ Natural Number

Then using the number sets in the booklet of formulae and tables or the information in the Chapter on number systems, we write:

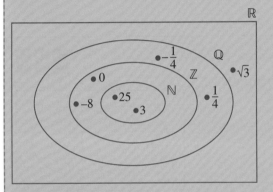

key point

The set $\mathbb{N}$ is a subset of the set $\mathbb{Z}$.

It is written $\mathbb{N} \subset \mathbb{Z}$.

Similarly,

$\mathbb{N} \subset \mathbb{Q}$ and $\mathbb{Z} \subset \mathbb{Q}$.

exam focus

This solution requires techniques from Indices and Number Systems in order to successfully complete the Venn diagram. This is typical of the questions that you will meet in the exam.

Set difference

To illustrate set difference, we consider two sets E and F where

$E = \{a, b, p, q, x, y\}$ and $F = \{a, b, c, d\}$.

If we remove from set E all the elements which are in set F, we have E less F.

E less F is denoted by $E \backslash F$.

We then write $E \backslash F = \{p, q, x, y\}$.

key point

$E \backslash F$ is the set of elements of E which are not in F.

We may illustrate set difference by Venn diagrams as follows:

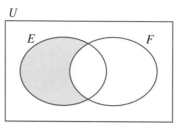

Shaded area is $E\backslash F$

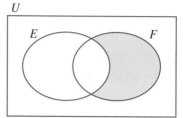

Shaded area is $F\backslash E$

Example

(i) From the Venn diagram list the elements of:

(a) $R \cup S$ (b) $S \cup R$

(c) $R\backslash S$ (d) $S\backslash R$

(ii) Using the results from part (i) explain why:

(a) Union of sets is commutative

(b) Set difference is not commutative

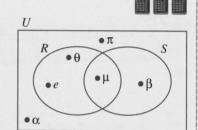

Solution

(i) (a) $R \cup S = \{e, \theta, \mu, \beta\}$

(b) $S \cup R = \{\beta, \mu, e, \theta\}$

(c) $R\backslash S = \{e, \theta\}$

(d) $S\backslash R = \{\beta\}$

(ii) (a) $R \cup S = S \cup R$ That is, when the order is reversed the answers are the same, so union of sets is commutative.

(b) $R\backslash S \neq S\backslash R$ That is, when the order is reversed the answers are not the same, so set difference is not commutative.

The cardinal number of a set (#)

The number of elements in a set is called the cardinal number of the set.

The symbol # is used to denote cardinal number.

If $E = \{p, q, r, s\}$, then $\# E = 4$.

Example

From the given Venn diagram, complete the following:

(i) A (ii) A'

(iii) $\#A$ (iv) $\#A'$

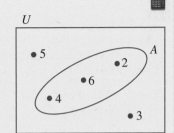

Solution   (i) $A = \{4, 6, 2\}$ (ii) $A' = \{5, 3\}$

(iii) $\#A = 3$ (iv) $\#A' = 2$

Example

In the given Venn diagram, each dot represents an element. Write down:

(i) $\#E$ (ii) $\#(E \cap F)$

(iii) $\#(F \backslash E)$ (iv) $\#F'$

(v) $\#[U \backslash (E \cup F)]$ (vi) $\#[(F \backslash E) \cup (E \backslash F)]$

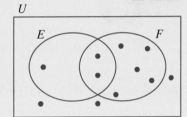

Solution   (i) $\#E = 3$ (ii) $\#(E \cap F) = 2$

(iii) $\#(F \backslash E) = 5$ (iv) $\#F' = 4$

(v) $\#[U \backslash (E \cup F)] = \#[(E \cup F)'] = 3$

(vi) U

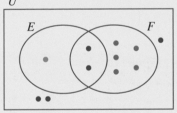 $\#[(F \backslash E) \cup (E \backslash F)] = 6$

Numerical problems on two sets

If some of the elements are not in any of the given sets, then we must introduce the universal set. Also, in many problems we may have to use a variable, say, x, to represent the number of elements in a region.

In numerical problems on sets:

- The symbol $\cap$ means **and**.
- The symbol $\cup$ means **or**.

A leisure centre has 110 members. The weights room (*W*) is used by 82 members and the swimming pool (*S*) is used by 57 members. 15 members do not use either facility.

Draw a Venn diagram and complete it to show the number of members in each part of each set.

Solution

Let the number of members who use both = x, i.e. $\#(W \cap S) = x$.

key point

When working with Venn diagrams, always work from the centre outwards.

$\Rightarrow \#(W \setminus S) = 82 - x$ and $\#(S \setminus W) = 57 - x$

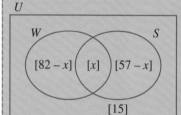

The total number of members

= $\#(U)$

= 110

Hence, $[82 - x] + [x] + [57 - x] + [15] = 110$

$$82 - x + x + 57 - x + 15 = 110$$

$$154 - x = 110$$

$$154 - 110 = x$$

$$44 = x$$

Finally:

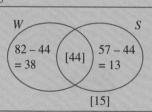

A group of 38 students were asked if they had ever been to France or Spain.

The number who had been to Spain only was three more than the number who had been to both countries.

Twice as many had been to France as Spain.

Four students had not been to either country.

Find how many had been to both countries.

Solution

Let x be the number of students who visited both countries.

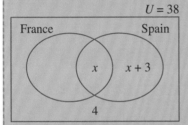

$(x + 3)$ went to Spain only

Total number who visited Spain $= x + (x + 3) = 2x + 3$.

Twice as many had been to France as Spain.

$\Rightarrow$ Number to France $= 2(\text{Spain}) = 2(2x + 3) = 4x + 6$.

$(4x + 6) - x$ went to France only

$(3x + 6)$ went to France only

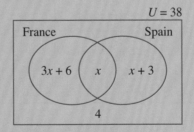

The total number of students in all four sections $= 38$.

$$\text{This means } (3x + 6) + x + (x + 3) + 4 = 38$$
$$5x + 13 = 38$$
$$5x = 38 - 13$$
$$5x = 25$$
$$x = 5$$

This means five students had been to both countries.

This question was a disaster for candidates. The total awarded for a correct solution was 5 marks, with 3 marks awarded for **any** one correct step.

Example

A and B are two sets such that $\#(A \cup B) = 46$ and $\#(A \cap B) = 11$. If $\#(A\backslash B) : \#(B\backslash A) = 4 : 3$, find $\#A$.

Solution

Let $\#(A\backslash B) = 4x$ and $\#(B\backslash A) = 3x$.

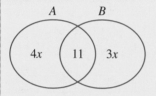

key point

In this solution, the universal set is not used as it is not required.

Given $\qquad A \cup B = 46$

Means $\qquad 4x + 11 + 3x = 46 \qquad$ Then $\quad \#A = 4x + 11$

$\qquad\qquad\qquad 7x = 46 - 11$

$\qquad\qquad\qquad 7x = 35 \qquad\qquad\qquad\qquad \#A = 4(5) + 11$

$\qquad\qquad\qquad\quad x = 5 \qquad\qquad\qquad\qquad \#A = 20 + 11$

$\qquad\qquad\qquad\qquad\qquad\qquad\qquad\qquad\qquad \#A = 31$

Maximum and minimum problems on two sets

The following is very useful when dealing with maximum and minimum problems on two sets.

key point

To maximise $\#(E \cup F)$, minimise $\#(E \cap F)$.

To minimise $\#(E \cup F)$, maximise $\#(E \cap F)$.

In a survey of tourists, 1 611 said they had visited the Cliffs of Moher and 946 had visited the Giant's Causeway. 113 had visited neither.

What is: **(i)** The greatest number that could have been surveyed?

(ii) The smallest number that could have been surveyed?

Solution

(i) Let x represent the number of tourists who visited both.

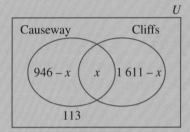

The total number surveyed is #U = $(946 - x) + x + (1\,611 - x) + 113$

$$= 2\,670 - x$$

The smallest value that x can have is zero.

When x is at a minimum, then #U is at a maximum.

Hence, the greatest number surveyed = #U = $2\,670 - 0 = 2\,670$.

(ii) The biggest value x can have is 946.

The biggest value x can have is the smaller of 946 and 1 611.

Hence, the least number surveyed = #U = $2\,670 - 946 = 1\,724$.

Example

From the Venn diagram:

(i) Name any three subsets of K.

(ii) What is the name of the set that is a subset of every set?

(iii) Without listing them, how many subsets would set

(a) K have in total

(b) J have in total?

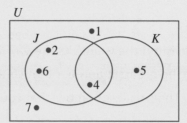

Solution

(i) Possible subsets of K include

$\{4\}$; $\{5\}$; $\{4, 5\}$; $\{\ \}$ – any three of these will answer the question.

(ii) The null set, $\{\ \}$, is always a subset of every set.

Also every set is a subset of itself.

(iii) (a) K has a total of four subsets, as listed in part (i).

> **key point**
>
> The total number of subsets is 2 to the power of the number of elements in the set.
>
> So K has $2^2 = 4$ subsets.

(b) From the key point above, the total number of subsets in J is $2^3 = 8$, i.e. 2 to the power of the number of elements in the set.

The question does not require a list of all the subsets of J, but here they are:

$\{\ \}$ $\{2, 4, 6\}$

$\{6\}$ $\{2\}$ $\{4\}$

$\{2, 6\}$ $\{4, 2\}$ $\{4, 6\}$

Numerical problems on three sets

We solve numerical problems on three sets in exactly the same way as those using two sets. With three sets we have more regions to deal with. As before, we may have to use a variable, say, x, if some information is missing. In more complicated problems we may have to use two variables, say, x and y.

The Venn diagram represents the sets

Natural numbers $\mathbb{N}$

Integers $\mathbb{Z}$

Rational numbers $\mathbb{Q}$

Real numbers $\mathbb{R}$

Insert each of the following numbers in the correct place on the diagram:

$8, 0, \pi, -126, \dfrac{2}{3}, -\dfrac{6}{5}, \sqrt{11}, 4, -9.$

Hence or otherwise, shade in the empty sets.

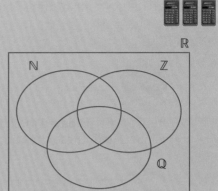

Solution

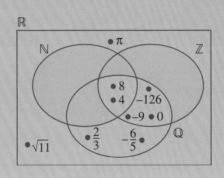

A poll was taken of the leisure time activities of 90 students.

60 students watch TV (T), 60 students read (R), 70 students go to the cinema (C).

26 students watch TV, read and go to the cinema.

20 students watch TV and go to the cinema only.

18 students read and go to the cinema only.

10 students read and watch TV only.

 (i) Draw a Venn diagram to illustrate the above information.

(ii) Calculate how many students:

   (a) Only watch TV.

   (b) Only go to the cinema.

(iii) Find the probability that a student chosen at random from the group had participated in none of the leisure time activities.

Solution (i)

26 students participated in all three leisure time activities. It is worth remembering in these situations that we work from the inside out.

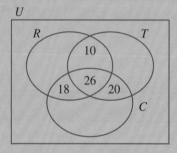 ⇒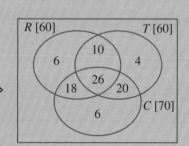

T only $= 60 - 10 - 26 - 20$
     $= 4$

R only $= 60 - 10 - 26 - 18$
     $= 6$

C only $= 70 - 18 - 26 - 20$
     $= 6$

(ii) (a) 4 only watch TV

   (b) 6 only go to cinema

(iii) Since $6 + 10 + 4 + 18 + 26 + 20 + 6 = 90$, every student took part in at least one leisure time activity.

   P (student selected at random took part in no activity) $= 0$.

Probability and Sets will often be seen together in exam questions. For more on this see *Less Stress More Success Junior Cycle Maths Book 2* and the section on Venn diagrams in the chapter on probability.

(a) *A, B,* and *C* are sets. Complete the tables below by shading in each of the given sets in the Venn diagram.

Set	$A \cup B$
Venn diagram	 *A* *B* *C*

Set	$A \backslash (B \cap C)$
Venn diagram	 *A* *B* *C*

(b) *P* and *Q* are two other sets. *P* is a subset of *Q*.

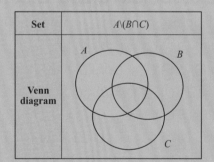

(i) Write an X in the region of the Venn diagram below which must contain no elements.

(ii) Put a tick (✓) in the correct box to show which statement must be true.

Tick one box only. Explain your answer.   # $P \leq$ # Q # $P =$ # Q # $P \geq$ # Q
☐ ☐ ☐

Solution

(a) $A \cup B$:
Shade the region that covers all the elements of *A* and all of the elements of *B*.

Set	$A \cup B$
Venn diagram	 *A* *B* *C*

$A \backslash (B \cap C)$:
Shade the region that covers the elements in *A*, except those that are in both *B* and *C*

Set	$A \backslash (B \cap C)$
Venn diagram	 *A* *B* *C*

(b) (i) If *P* is a subset of *Q*, then all of the elements of *P* are also in *Q*. So, the region where the elements of '*P* only' would be will be empty.

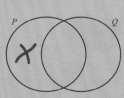

(ii) If *P* is a subset of *Q*, then all of the elements of *P* are also in *Q*. Therefore, the number of elements in *P* must be equal to, or less than, the number of elements in *Q*.

$P \leq$ # Q # $P =$ # Q # $P \geq$ # Q
✓ ☐ ☐

$U = \{2, 3, 4, 5, \ldots, 30\}$, $A = \{$multiples of 2$\}$, $B = \{$multiples of 3$\}$,

$C = \{$multiples of 5$\}$.

(i) Find #[$(A \cup B \cup C)'$], the number of elements in the complement of the set $A \cup B \cup C$.

(ii) How many divisors does each of the numbers in $(A \cup B \cup C)'$ have?

(iii) What name is given to numbers that have this many divisors?

Solution

(i) $A = \{2, 4, 6, \ldots \ldots 30\}$

  $B = \{3, 6, 9, \ldots \ldots 30\}$

  $C = \{5, 10, 15, 20, 25, 30\}$

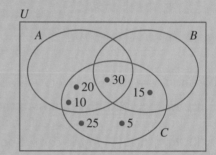

$A \cup B \cup C = \{2, 3, 4, 5, 6, \not{7}, 8, 9, 10, \not{11}, 12, \not{13}, 14, 15, 16, \not{17}, 18, \not{19}, 20, 21, 22, \not{23}, 24, 25, 26, 27, 28, \not{29}, 30\}$

$(A \cup B \cup C)' = \{7, 11, 13, 17, 19, 23, 29\}$ Hence, #[$(A \cup B \cup C)'$] = 7

(ii) Two divisors   **(iii)** Prime numbers

The associative and distributive properties in sets

The following statements are worth noting:

① $A \cup (B \cup C) = (A \cup B) \cup C$ Associative property

② $A \cap (B \cap C) = (A \cap B) \cap C$ Associative property

③ $A \setminus (B \setminus C) \neq (A \setminus B) \setminus C$

④ $A \cap (B \cup C) = (A \cap B) \cup (A \cap C)$ Distributive property

⑤ $A \cup (B \cap C) = (A \cup B) \cap (A \cup C)$ Distributive property

⑥ $A \setminus (B \cap C) \neq (A \setminus B) \cap (A \setminus C)$

① and ② Indicate the operations union and intersection are associative

③   Indicates the operation set difference is **not** associative

④   Indicates the intersection of sets is distributive over union

⑤   Indicates the union of sets is distributive over intersection

⑥   Indicates set difference is **not** distributive

Example

Using the distributive property, complete the following true statements:

(i) $X \cup (Y \cap Z) =$

(ii) $H \cap (J \cup K) =$

(iii) $\qquad = (D \cup F) \cap (D \cup E)$

Solution   (i) $X \cup (Y \cap Z) = (X \cup Y) \cap (X \cup Z)$

(ii) $H \cap (J \cup K) = (H \cap J) \cup (H \cap K)$

(iii) $D \cup (F \cap E) = (D \cup F) \cap (D \cup E)$

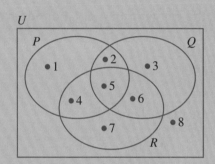

(i) From the Venn diagram above, list the elements of:

(a) $P \cup Q$

(b) $Q \cap R$

(c) $P \cup (Q \cap R)$

(ii) Miriam says: 'For all sets, union is distributive over intersection.' Name a set that you would use along with $P \cup (Q \cap R)$ to show that Miriam's claim is true for the sets P, Q and R in the Venn diagram above.

Solution

(i) (a) $P \cup Q = \{1, 2, 3, 4, 5, 6\}$

(b) $Q \cap R = \{5, 6\}$

(c) $P \cup (Q \cap R) = \{1, 2, 4, 5\} \cup \{5, 6\}$

$\qquad\qquad\qquad = \{1, 2, 4, 5, 6\}$

(ii) $P \cup (Q \cap R) = (P \cup Q) \cap (P \cup R)$

Example

Using the Venn diagram on the right, solve for x and y if

$\# A = 40$ and $\# [(A \cup C) \setminus B] = 26$.

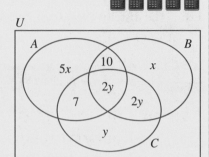

Solution

$\# A = 40$ means $5x + 10 + 2y + 7 = 40$

$$5x + 2y = 40 - 17$$
$$5x + 2y = 23 \quad ①$$

Now, $\# [(A \cup C) \setminus B] = 26$.

$(A \cup C) \setminus B$ means all the elements in A or C but **not** in B.

This gives us $5x + 7 + y = 26$.

$$5x + y = 26 - 7$$
$$5x + y = 19 \quad ②$$

Now we solve the simultaneous equations ① and ②.

$5x + 2y = 23$	①	$5x + 2y = 23$	①
$5x + \;\;y = 19$	②		
$y = 4$	(subtract)	$5x + 2(4) = 23$	
		$5x + 8 = 23$	
		$5x = 23 - 8$	
		$5x = 15$	
		$x = 3$	

This solution requires techniques from Simultaneous Equations as well as Sets to arrive at a successful conclusion. This is a classic exam-type question.

Three problems *A*, *B* and *C* were given to a set of pupils. The numbers in the brackets are the cardinal numbers of the different sets, e.g. 31 solved problem *A*, 21 solved *B*, 5 solved all three problems, etc. Each pupil solved at least one problem.

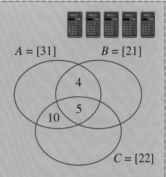

$A = [31]$ $B = [21]$

4

5

10

$C = [22]$

(i) How many pupils solved *A* only?
Find the **(ii)** maximum **(iii)** minimum number of pupils that could have solved *A* or *B* or *C*.

Solution

(i) How many solved *A* only?

The number who solved *A* only = 31 − 4 − 5 − 10 = 31 − 19 = 12.

(ii) The maximum that could have solved *A* or *B* or *C* ⟹ # ($A \cup B \cup C$) maximum.
To maximise # ($A \cup B \cup C$) we minimise # [($B \cap C$) \ *A*].

key point

We saw earlier that in order to maximise a union of sets, we minimise (the remaining) intersection region, which in this case is ($B \cap C$) \ *A*, as the numbers in set *A* are already decided.

The minimum of # [($B \cap C$) \ *A*] = 0, hence the number who solved *B* only = 21 − 4 − 5 − 0 = 12 and the number who solved *C* only = 22 − 10 − 5 − 0 = 7

Then the maximum number that could have solved *A* or *B* or *C*
= 12 + 4 + 12 + 10 + 5 + 0 + 7
= 50

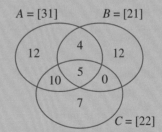

$A = [31]$ $B = [21]$

12

4

12

10

5

0

7

$C = [22]$

(iii) The minimum that could have solved *A* or *B* or *C* ⟹ # ($A \cup B \cup C$) minimum. To minimise # ($A \cup B \cup C$) we maximise # [($B \cap C$) \ *A*].

key point

We saw earlier that in order to minimise a union of sets, we maximise (the remaining) intersection region, which in this case is ($B \cap C$) \ *A*, as the numbers in set *A* are already fixed.

The maximum of # [(B ∩ C) \ A] = 7, that is, the smallest number from 7 remaining in set C or 12 remaining in set B.

Hence the number who solved B only = 21 − 4 − 5 − 7 = 5 and the number who solved C only = 22 − 10 − 5 − 7 = 0.

Then the minimum number that could have solved A or B or C

= 12 + 4 + 5 + 10 + 5 + 7 + 0

= 43

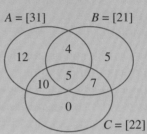

$A = [31]$ $B = [21]$

12   4   5

10   5   7

0

$C = [22]$

Put a tick (✓) in the correct box in each row of the table below to show whether each statement is always true, sometimes true, or never true, for three different sets A, B, and C.

Statement	Tick **one** box only, for each statement		
	Always true	Sometimes true	Never true
$A \cap B = B \cap A$			
$A \cup B = B \cup C$			
$A \cap (B \cup C) = (A \cap B) \cup (A \cap C)$			
$A \cup C = A \cap C$			
$A \backslash B = \{\ \}$			

Solution

Statement	Tick **one** box only, for each statement		
	Always true	Sometimes true	Never true
$A \cap B = B \cap A$	✓		
$A \cup B = B \cup C$		✓	
$A \cap (B \cup C) = (A \cap B) \cup (A \cap C)$	✓		
$A \cup C = A \cap C$			✓
$A \backslash B = \{\ \}$		✓	

13 Functions

□ To learn what a function is and how to recognise one.
□ To become familiar with the notation associated with functions.
□ To be able to solve problems involving functions.

A function is a rule that changes one number (input) into another number (output). Functions are often represented by the letters f, g, h or k. We can think of a function, f, as a number machine which changes an input, x, into an output, $f(x)$.

Input

Output

$f(x)$, which denotes the output, is read as 'f of x'.

key point

A function is also called a **mapping** or simply a **map**.

For example, let's represent the function 'double input and then add 5' by the letter f. This can be written as:

$$f:x \rightarrow 2x + 5 \quad \text{or} \quad f(x) = 2x + 5 \quad \text{or} \quad y = 2x + 5$$

$$(\text{input, output}) = (x, f(x)) = (x, 2x + 5) = (x, y)$$

key point

Note the different notations for function: $f : x \rightarrow$, $f(x)$, y.

One number is mapped onto another number.
In the above example, x is mapped onto $2x + 5$, usually written $f : x \rightarrow 2x + 5$.
A function connects every input (x) in the domain to an output $(f(x))$ in the range.
A function is another way of writing an algebraic formula that links input (x) to output $(f(x))$.

Types of functions		
Linear	$f : x \rightarrow ax$ or	$f : x \rightarrow ax + b$
Quadratic	$f : x \rightarrow ax^2 + bx + c$	
Exponential	$f : x \rightarrow ab^x$	

Input number

If $f: x \longrightarrow 2x + 5$, then $f(3)$ means 'input 3 into the function', i.e. it is the result of applying the function f to the number 3.

$$f(3) = 2(3) + 5 = 6 + 5 = 11 \qquad (\text{input} = 3, \text{output} = 11)$$
$$(\text{input, output}) = (3, f(3)) = (3, 11)$$

key point

> A function performs the exact same procedure to each input number and produces only one output number for each input number.

The set of input numbers is called the **domain**. The set of output numbers is called the **range**. The set of **all possible outputs** is called the **codomain**. In general, the range is a subset of the codomain. However, sometimes the range and the codomain are the same.

Consider the function f shown:

$$f = \{(1, a), (2, b), (3, d), (4, d)\}$$

from set X to set Y.

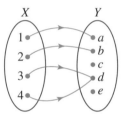

Domain: The set of elements from which the arrows leave: $\{1, 2, 3, 4\}$.
Range: The set of elements where the arrows arrive: $\{a, b, d\}$.
Codomain: The **possible** set of elements into which the arrows go: $\{a, b, c, d, e\}$.

Consider the function:

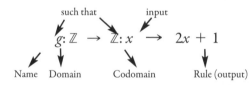

key point

> A domain or range described as:
>
> $$[p, q) \text{ means } \{p \leq x < q\}$$
>
> That is, the square bracket means p is included.
> The rounded bracket means q is **not** included.

key point

> **To recognise if a mapping represents a function:**
>
> - If any element in the domain has no arrow, then it is **not** a function.
> - If any element in the domain has more than one arrow leaving it, it is **not** a function.
> - Therefore, **a mapping represents a function if there is exactly one arrow leaving every element in the domain.**

Example

State whether each of the following mapping diagrams is a function.
Give a reason for your answer in each case.

(i) 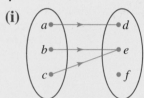 **(ii)**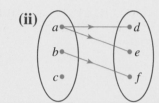

(iii) 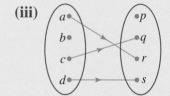 **(iv)**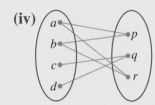

Solution

(i) Is a function, as each input has only one unique output.

(ii) Is not a function, as input a has two outputs. Also input c has no output.

(iii) Is not a function, as one element in the domain, input b, has no output.

(iv) Is not a function, as inputs a and b have more than one output.

Example

A function f is defined as $f: x \rightarrow 3x - 2$.
Find the missing numbers, p, q and r.

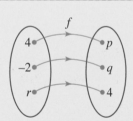

Solution

$f: x \rightarrow 3x - 2$

$f(4) = 3(4) - 2$

$\quad = 12 - 2$

$\quad = 10$

$\therefore \quad p = 10$

$f: x \rightarrow 3x - 2$

$f(-2) = 3(-2) - 2$

$\quad = -6 - 2$

$\quad = -8$

$\therefore \quad q = -8$

To find r, we are given an equation in disguise
Output $= 4$, find input r:

$f(x) = 4$

$3x - 2 = 4$

$3x = 6$

$x = 2$

$\therefore \quad r = 2$

key point

Substituting and solving equations are vital skills for you to have when working with functions. Working with functions follows the same procedure as substituting and solving equations in Algebra. These were covered in earlier chapters.

Example

A function f is defined as $f: x \rightarrow 3 + 2x$.

Find: **(i)** $f(0)$ **(ii)** $f(1)$ **(iii)** $f(2)$ **(iv)** $f(-1) - f(0)$ **(v)** Verify that $f(3) > 0$.

Solution

(i) $f(x) = 3 + 2x$

$f(0) = 3 + 2(0)$

$f(0) = 3 + 0$

$f(0) = 3$

(ii) $f(x) = 3 + 2x$

$f(1) = 3 + 2(1)$

$f(1) = 3 + 2$

$f(1) = 5$

(iii) $f(x) = 3 + 2x$

$f(2) = 3 + 2(2)$

$f(2) = 3 + 4$

$f(2) = 7$

(iv) Find $f(-1) - f(0)$:

$f(x) = 3 - 2x$

$f(-1) = 3 + 2(-1)$

$f(-1) = 3 - 2$

$f(-1) = 1$ and $f(0) = 3$ (from **(i)**)

$\therefore f(-1) - f(0) = 1 - 3 = -2$

(v) Find $f(3)$ and see if it is greater than zero:

$f(3) = 3 + 2(3)$

$f(3) = 3 + 6$

$f(3) = 9$ which is greater than zero

$\therefore f(3) > 0$

Example

A function f is defined as $f : x \rightarrow 2x - 5$. Complete the following four couples:

(i) $(3, \ )$ (ii) $(-3, \ )$ (iii) $(\ , 3)$ (iv) $(\ , 7)$

Solution

(i) $f : x \rightarrow 2x - 5$ $(3, \ )$

When $x = 3$, find y:
$f(3) = 2(3) - 5$
$= 6 - 5$
$= 1$
Therefore, the couple is $(3, 1)$.

(ii) $f : x \rightarrow 2x - 5$ $(-3, \ )$

When $x = -3$, find y:
$f(-3) = 2(-3) - 5$
$= -6 - 5$
$= -11$
Therefore, the couple is $(-3, -11)$.

(iii) $f : x \rightarrow 2x - 5$ $(\ , 3)$

When $y = 3$, find x:
$3 = 2x - 5$
$3 + 5 = 2x$
$8 = 2x$
$4 = x$
Therefore, the couple is $(4, 3)$.

(iv) $f : x \rightarrow 2x - 5$ $(\ , 7)$

When $y = 7$, find x:
$7 = 2x - 5$
$7 + 5 = 2x$
$12 = 2x$
$6 = x$
Therefore, the couple is $(6, 7)$.

The picture shows a wheel with six spokes. The spokes are labelled A, B, C, D, E and F.

(i) The wheel is rotated anti-clockwise so that the point A is mapped onto point C. What is the angle of rotation?

(ii) Complete the following ordered pairs, where the input value is the original position and the output value is the mapped position.

$\{(A, C), (B, \ ), (\ , E), (\ , \ ), (\ , \ ), (\ , \ )\}$

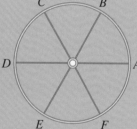

Solution

(i) Since there are six spokes, the wheel is divided into six sectors.

Angle in each sector $= \dfrac{360}{6} = 60°$

Rotating the wheel anti-clockwise so that point A moves to point C means it has been rotated by two sectors. Therefore, the angle of rotation $= 2(60°) = 120°$.

(ii) A moves to C, B moves to D, C moves to E, D moves to F, E moves to A and F moves to B.

So the ordered pairs are: $\{(A, C), (B, D), (C, E), (D, F), (E, A), (F, B)\}$.

Let $f(x) = 3x + 5$, for $x \in \mathbb{R}$.

(i) Find the value of $f(7)$.

(ii) Write $f(k)$ in terms of k.

(iii) Using your answer to part (ii), or otherwise, find the value of k for which $f(k) = k$.

Solution

(i) $f(x) = 3x + 5$

$f(7) = 3(7) + 5$

$f(7) = 21 + 5$

$f(7) = 26$

(ii) $f(x) = 3x + 5$

$f(k) = 3k + 5$

(iii) $f(k) = k$

$3k + 5 = k$

$3k - k = -5$

$2k = -5$

$k = -2 \cdot 5$

A school is planning a trip to a local museum. They are taking the school's mini-bus. It will cost €42 for parking for the bus during the day. Tickets to enter the museum are €16·50 per student.

(i) Find the total cost of the trip in terms of n, where n equals the number of students who go on the trip

(ii) Find the total cost of the trip for 20 students.

(iii) Find the cost of the trip, per student, if 14 students go on the trip.

(iv) If the total cost of the trip came to €339, how many students went on the trip?

Solution

(i) n = Number of students

Cost = Cost of parking + ticket per student

$c(n) = €42 + €16 \cdot 50(n)$

(ii) Find the cost when $n = 20$: $c(n) = €42 + €16 \cdot 50(n)$

$c(20) = €42 + €16 \cdot 50(20)$

$c(20) = €42 + €330$

$c(20) = €372$

Therefore, the trip will cost €372 for a group of 20 students.

key point

Notice that this is actually a fairly straightforward Pattern question.

(iii) Find the cost when $n = 14$: $\quad c(n) = €42 + €16\cdot50(n)$

$$c(14) = €42 + €16\cdot50(14)$$

$$c(14) = €42 + €231$$

$$c(14) = €273$$

Therefore, the trip will cost €273 for a group of 14 students.

Cost per student = €273 ÷ 14 = €19·50 per student.

(iv) Find n when $c(n) = 339$: $\quad c(n) = €42 + €16\cdot50(n)$

$$€339 = €42 + €16\cdot50(n)$$

$$€339 - €42 = €16\cdot50(n)$$

$$€297 = €16\cdot50(n) \qquad (\div\ 16\cdot50)$$

$$18 = n$$

Therefore, 18 students went on the trip.

Let g be the function $g : x \rightarrow 2^{x-3}$. Find the value of $g(3)$.

Solution

$g(x) = 2^{x-3}$

$g(3) = 2^{3-3}$

$g(3) = 2^0$

$g(3) = 1 \qquad$ (using calculator or rule of indices, that $a^0 = 1$)

$g: x \rightarrow 9 - x^2$ is a function defined on $\mathbb{R}$.

(i) What is $g(-4)$?

(ii) What is $3[g(2)]$?

(iii) Find the values of x for which $g(x) = 0$.

Solution

(i)　$g(x) = 9 - x^2$

　$g(-4) = 9 - (-4)^2$

　$g(-4) = 9 - 16$

　$g(-4) = -7$

(ii)　$g(x) = 9 - x^2$

　$g(2) = 9 - (2)^2$

　$g(2) = 9 - 4$

　$g(2) = 5$

　$3[g(2)] = 3[5]$

　$3[g(2)] = 15$

(iii)　$g(x) = 9 - x^2$

　$0 = 9 - x^2$

　$0 = 3^2 - x^2$

　$0 = (3 - x)(3 + x)$

　$0 = 3 - x$　or　$0 = 3 + x$

　$x = 3$　　　　$-3 = x$

Solving a quadratic equation is a vital skill to have throughout your course. Solving quadratic equations was covered in an earlier chapter.

Let f be the function $f: x \rightarrow 1 - 3x$ and g be the function $g: x \rightarrow 1 - x^2$.

(i) Find $f(-2)$ and $g(5)$.

(ii) Express $f(x + 1)$ in the form $ax + b$, a and $b \in \mathbb{Z}$.

(iii) Solve for x: $f(x + 1) = f(-2) + g(5)$.

Solution

(i)　$f(x) = 1 - 3x$　　$g(x) = 1 - x^2$

　$f(-2) = 1 - 3(-2)$　$g(5) = 1 - x^2$

　$f(-2) = 1 + 6$　　　$g(5) = 1 - (5)^2$

　$f(-2) = 7$　　　　　$g(5) = 1 - 25$

　　　　　　　　　　　$g(5) = -24$

Marking scheme for this question was:

(i) 10 marks (ii) 5 marks (iii) 5 marks

However, you couldn't answer (iii) without (ii).

(ii) $f(x) = 1 - 3x$
$f(x + 1) = 1 - 3(x + 1)$
$f(x + 1) = 1 - 3x - 3$
$f(x + 1) = -2 - 3x$

(iii) $f(x + 1) = f(-2) + g(5)$
$-2 - 3x = 7 - 24$
$-3x = 7 - 24 + 2$
$-3x = -15$
$x = 5$

$h : x \rightarrow 3x + p$ and $k : x \rightarrow 4x^2 - p$ are two functions defined on $\mathbb{R}$, where $p \in \mathbb{Z}$.

(i) If $h(2) = 4$, find the value of p.

(ii) Find the two values of x for which $h(x) + k(x) = 0$.

Solution

(i) $h(x) = 3x + p$
$h(2) = 3(2) + p$
$4 = 6 + p$
$-2 = p$

(ii) Given that $p = -2$: $h : x \rightarrow 3x - 2$ and $k : x \rightarrow 4x^2 - (-2)$
$k : x \rightarrow 4x^2 + 2$

$$h(x) + k(x) = 0$$
$$(3x - 2) + (4x^2 + 2) = 0$$
$$3x - 2 + 4x^2 + 2 = 0$$
$$4x^2 + 3x = 0$$
$$x(4x + 3) = 0$$
$$x = 0 \quad \text{or} \quad 4x + 3 = 0$$
$$4x = -3$$
$$x = -\frac{3}{4}$$

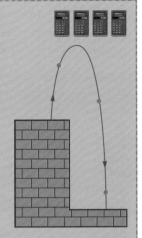

A ball is thrown into the air. Its height above the ground, h (measured in metres), at any given time after the ball is thrown, t (measured in seconds), can be modelled using the quadratic function $h(t) = -4t^2 + 20t + 23$.

  (i) From what height above the ground was the ball thrown?
 (ii) Find the height of the ball above the ground after 5·5 seconds.
(iii) Find the two times when the height of the ball is 39 m.

Solution

(i) The ball is thrown when $t = 0$ seconds. Find h when $t = 0$:
$$h(t) = -4t^2 + 20t + 23$$
$$h(0) = -4(0)^2 + 20(0) + 23$$
$$h(0) = 23$$

Therefore, at the start, the ball was at a height of 23 m.

(ii) Find h when $t = 5 \cdot 5$: $h(t) = -4t^2 + 20t + 23$
$$h(5{\cdot}5) = -4(5{\cdot}5)^2 + 20(5{\cdot}5) + 23$$
$$h(5{\cdot}5) = -4(30{\cdot}25) + 110 + 23$$
$$h(5{\cdot}5) = -121 + 133$$
$$h(5{\cdot}5) = 12$$

Therefore, after 5·5 seconds, the ball was at a height of 12 m.

(iii) Find t when $h = 39$ m: $h(t) = -4t^2 + 20t + 23$
$$39 = -4t^2 + 20t + 23$$
$$4t^2 - 20t - 23 + 39 = 0$$
$$4t^2 - 20t + 16 = 0 \qquad \text{(divide by 4)}$$
$$t^2 - 5t + 4 = 0$$
$$(t - 4)(t - 1) = 0$$
$$t - 4 = 0 \quad \text{or} \quad t - 1 = 0$$
$$t = 4 \qquad\qquad t = 1$$

Therefore, the height of the ball is 39 m after 1 second (going up) and after 4 seconds (coming down).

Example

A function f is defined as $f : x \rightarrow 3(2)^x$, where $x \in \mathbb{R}$.

Find: (i) $f(1)$ (ii) $f(0)$ (iii) $f(-2)$ (iv) Find the value of x for which $f(x) = 96$.

Solution

(i) $f(x) = 3(2)^x$

$f(1) = 3(2)^1$

$f(1) = 3(2) \qquad (2^1 = 2)$

$f(1) = 6$

(ii) $f(x) = 3(2)^x$

$f(0) = 3(2)^0$

$f(0) = 3(1) \qquad (2^0 = 1)$

$f(0) = 3$

(iii) $f(x) = 3(2)^x$

$f(-2) = 3(2)^{-2}$

$f(-2) = 3\left(\dfrac{1}{2^2}\right)$

$f(-2) = 3\left(\dfrac{1}{4}\right)$

$f(-2) = \dfrac{3}{4}$

(iv) $f(x) = 3(2)^x$

$96 = 3(2)^x$

$32 = (2)^x \qquad$ (divide both sides by 3)

$2^5 = 2^x \qquad$ (from indices $32 = 2^5$)

$5 = x$

exam
Q

Let f be the function $f : x \rightarrow x^2 - 3x$.

(i) Express $f(t)$ and $f(2t + 1)$ in terms of t.

(ii) Hence, find the values of t for which $f(t) = f(2t + 1)$.

Solution

(i) $f(x) = x^2 - 3x$

$f(t) = t^2 - 3t$

$f(x) = x^2 - 3x$

$f(2t + 1) = (2t + 1)^2 - 3(2t + 1)$

$f(2t + 1) = 4t^2 + 4t + 1 - 6t - 3$

$f(2t + 1) = 4t^2 - 2t - 2$

(ii) $f(t) = f(2t + 1)$

$t^2 - 3t = 4t^2 - 2t - 2$

$0 = 3t^2 + t - 2$

$0 = (3t - 2)(t + 1)$

$0 = 3t - 2$ or $0 = t + 1$

$2 = 3t$ or $-1 = t$

$\dfrac{2}{3} = t$ or $-1 = t$

The number of bacteria in a test tube can be estimated with the model

$$B(n) = 45(2^n)$$

where $B(n)$ is the number of bacteria after n 20-minute intervals.

 (i) Use the model to estimate the number of bacteria present after 1 hour.

 (ii) Use the model to estimate the number of bacteria present after 4 hours.

(iii) Use the model to find how long until there will be 1 440 bacteria.

Solution

 (i) 1 hour = three 20-minute intervals, so let $n = 3$: $B(n) = 45(2^n)$

$B(3) = 45(2^3)$

$B(3) = 360$

Therefore, there will be 360 bacteria present after 1 hour.

(ii) 4 hours = twelve 20-minute intervals, so let $n = 12$: $B(n) = 45(2^n)$

$B(12) = 45(2^{12})$

$B(12) = 184\ 320$

Therefore, there will be 184 320 bacteria present after 4 hours.

(iii) To find the time taken for 1 440 bacteria: find n when $B(n) = 1\ 440$:

$$B(n) = 45(2^n)$$
$$1\ 440 = 45(2^n) \qquad \text{(let } (B(n) = 1\ 440)$$
$$32 = 2^n \qquad \text{(divide both sides by 45)}$$
$$2^5 = 2^n \qquad \text{(let } 32 = 2^5)$$
$$5 = n \qquad \text{(equate powers)}$$

There will be 1 440 bacteria present after five 20-minute intervals.

Thus, after 1 hour 40 minutes, there will be 1 440 bacteria present.

$g: x \rightarrow ax^2 + bx + 1$ is a function defined on $\mathbb{R}$.

(i) If $g(1) = 0$ and $g(2) = 3$, write down two equations in a and b.

(ii) Hence, calculate the value of a and the value of b.

Solution

(i) We are told $g(1) = 0$:

$g(x) = ax^2 + bx + 1$

$g(1) = a(1)^2 + b(1) + 1$

$\quad 0 = a(1) + b + 1 \qquad (g(1) = 0)$

$-1 = a + b \qquad\qquad$ equation ①

We are told $g(2) = 3$:

$g(x) = ax^2 + bx + 1$

$g(2) = a(2)^2 + b(2) + 1$

$\quad 3 = a(4) + 2b + 1 \qquad (g(2) = 3)$

$\quad 3 = 4a + 2b + 1$

$\quad 2 = 4a + 2b$

$\quad 1 = 2a + b \qquad\qquad$ equation ②

(ii) Solving the equations simultaneously:

① $\quad -1 = a + b \qquad (x - 1)$

② $\quad \dfrac{1 = 2a + b}{}$

$\quad 1 = -a - b$

$\quad \dfrac{1 = 2a + b}{2 = a}$

$-1 = a + b$

$-1 = 2 + b \qquad$ (let $a = 2$)

$-3 = b$

The process of solving simultaneous equations was covered in an earlier chapter.

Graphing Functions

aims
- ☐ To be able to graph functions of various forms.
- ☐ To be able to use the graphs to find the solution to given questions.

Graphing functions

To graph a function, find points which satisfy the function by substituting values in for *x* and finding the corresponding *y*-values. Plot these points and join them up to obtain the graph of the function.

key point

To better understand the graphs of functions, you should practise graphing functions on a graphing calculator or graphing software, such as GeoGebra (free to download from www.geogebra.org).

Linear functions

A linear function is usually given by $f : x \rightarrow ax + b$, where $a, b, \in \mathbb{Q}, x \in \mathbb{R}$.

To graph a linear function, you need two points.

If the coefficient of the *x* part is positive ($a > 0$), the graph is **increasing**:	If the coefficient of the *x* part is zero ($a = 0$), the graph is **horizontal**:	If the coefficient of the *x* part is negative ($a \subset 0$), the graph is **decreasing**:
e.g. $y = 2x + 3$	e.g. $y = 3$	e.g. $y = -2x + 3$
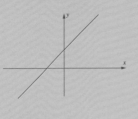		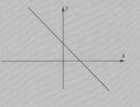

key point

Graphing linear functions is covered extensively under the topic of Coordinate Geometry of the Line, which can be found in *Less Stress More Success Junior Cycle Maths Book 2*. There is also a connection between linear functions and arithmetic patterns.

Example

(i) Using the same axes and scale, graph the functions $y = 3 - x$ and $2y = x + 3$ in the domain $-5 \leq x \leq 5$.

(ii) Use your graph to estimate the point of intersection between these two functions.

Solution

(i) In order to graph a linear function, find the two points at the end of each line segment.

Line 1: $y = 3 - x$		**Line 2: $2y = x + 3$**	
If $x = -5$:	If $x = 5$:	If $x = -5$:	If $x = 5$:
$y = 3 - (-5)$	$y = 3 - 5$	$2y = -5 + 3$	$2y = 5 + 3$
$y = 8$	$y = -2$	$2y = -2$	$2y = 8$
$(-5, 8)$	$(5, -2)$	$y = -1$	$y = 4$
		$(-5, -1)$	$(5, 4)$

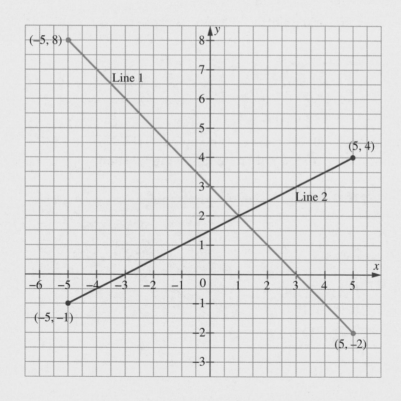

(ii) From the graph, we can estimate the point of intersection of the functions to be $(1, 2)$.

A taxi has a base starting charge of €4. The passenger is then charged an additional €1·50 for every kilometre travelled.

(i) Write a function for the cost of a trip in terms of k, where k is the number of kilometres travelled.

(ii) Graph the function in the domain from 0 km to 16 km.

(iii) Use your graph to find the cost of a trip that lasted 12 km.

(iv) Use your graph to find the distance covered during a trip which cost €13.

Solution

(i) Cost of a trip = Base charge of €4 + €1·50 per kilometre

$$c = €4 + €1·50(k)$$
$$c = 4 + 1·5(k)$$

(ii) Find the start and end points.

When $k = 0$ km:

$$c = 4 + 1·5(k)$$
$$c = 4 + 1·5(0)$$
$$c = 4 + 0$$
$$c = 4$$

When $k = 16$ km:

$$c = 4 + 1·5(k)$$
$$c = 4 + 1·5(16)$$
$$c = 4 + 24$$
$$c = 28$$

Start point: (0, 4)   End point: (16, 28)

Graph these points and join them to graph the function:

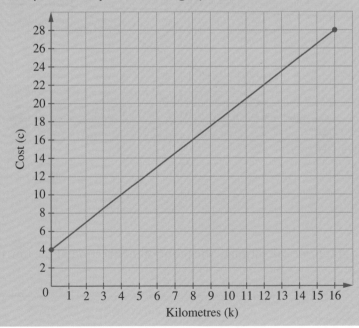

key point

A linear function can be represented by:

y = starting value + (rate of growth)x

This is the same as a linear or arithmetic pattern.

It is also the same as the equation of a line.

y = mx + c

where *m* = rate of growth = slope

c = starting value = *y*-intercept

(see booklet of formulae and tables)

(iii) From the graph (red line), when the number of kilometres *k* = 12, the cost equals €22.

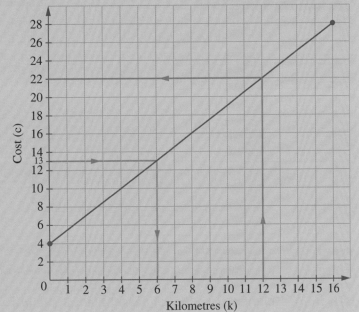

(iv) From the graph (green line), when the cost equals €13, the number of kilometres equals 6.

exam Q

Kevin is given two plants. One plant is 6 cm high and the other is 21 cm high. Kevin measures the height of each plant at the same time every day for a week. He notes that the 6 cm plant grows 3 cm each day and the 21 cm plant grows 1·5 cm each day.

(i) Draw a table showing the heights of the two plants each day for the week. Start on the day that John got them.

(ii) Write down two functions, one for each plant, to represent the plant's height on any given day. State clearly the meaning of any letters used in your formulas.

(iii) Draw graphs to represent the heights of the two plants over the first two weeks.

(iv) From your diagram, write down the point of intersection of the two graphs. Explain what the point of intersection means with respect to the two plants. Your answer should refer to the meaning of *both* coordinates.

(v) By solving the functions formed in part **(ii)** simultaneously, verify your answer to part **(iv)**.

(vi) Kevin's model for the growth of the plants might not be correct. State one limitation of the model that might affect the point of intersection and its interpretation.

Solution

(i) Start at day zero. On day one, the heights of the plants have increased by 3 cm and 1·5 cm respectively:

Plant A	
Day	**Height**
0	6
1	9
2	12
3	15
4	18
5	21
6	24

Plant B	
Day	**Height**
0	21
1	22.5
2	24
3	25.5
4	27
5	28.5
6	30

(ii) Plant A: Height = 6 + 3(no. of days)   Plant B: Height = 21 + 1·5(no. of days)

Plant A: $h = 6 + 3d$ Plant B: $h = 21 + 1·5d$

key
point

Remember:

y = (starting value) + (rate of growth)(x)

(iii) Graphing the growth of both plants over two weeks (14 days):

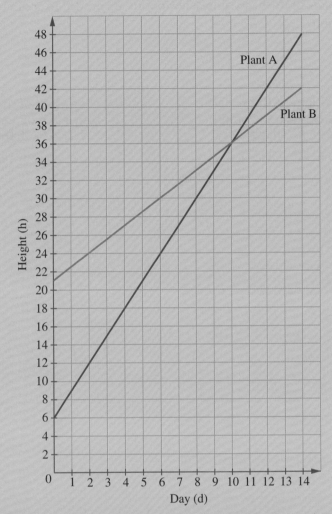

(iv) From the graphs we can estimate the point of intersection to be (10, 36). This means that on day 10, both plants are at a height of 36 cm.

(v) Solving the equations: $h = 6 + 3d$ and $h = 21 + 1{\cdot}5d$

Let $h = h$: $6 + 3d = 21 + 1{\cdot}5d$ Let $d = 10$:

$3d - 1{\cdot}5d = 21 - 6$ $h = 6 + 3d$

$1{\cdot}5d = 15$ $(\div 1{\cdot}5)$ $h = 6 + 3(10)$

$d = 10$ $h = 36$

Therefore, the point of intersection is (10, 36).

(vi) Kevin's model assumes that the plants continue to grow at a constant rate over a number of weeks. In reality you would expect the rate of growth to slow down. Other factors, such as amount of light and water, could affect the growth rate also.

Quadratic functions

A quadratic function is usually given by $f : x \rightarrow ax^2 + bx + c$, where $a, b, c \in \mathbb{Q}, x \in \mathbb{R}$ and $a \neq 0$. Because of its shape, quite a few points are needed to accurately graph a quadratic function.

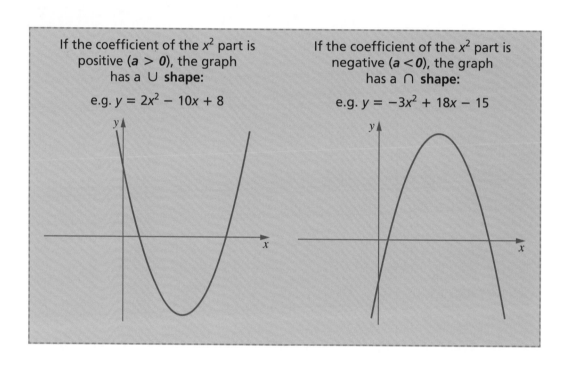

If the coefficient of the x^2 part is positive ($a > 0$), the graph has a $\cup$ **shape:**

e.g. $y = 2x^2 - 10x + 8$

If the coefficient of the x^2 part is negative ($a < 0$), the graph has a $\cap$ **shape:**

e.g. $y = -3x^2 + 18x - 15$

key point

The values where the graph of a quadratic function crosses the x-axis are known as the roots of the function.

These are the values you get when you solve the quadratic equation formed by letting the function equal zero.

Example

Draw a graph of the function $f : x \rightarrow x^2 + 3x - 1$ in the domain $-5 \leq x \leq 2$.

Solution

Complete a table:

x	$x^2 + 3x - 1$	y
-5	$(-5)^2 + 3(-5) - 1$	9
-4	$(-4)^2 + 3(-4) - 1$	3
-3	$(-3)^2 + 3(-3) - 1$	-1
-2	$(-2)^2 + 3(-2) - 1$	-3
-1	$(-1)^2 + 3(-1) - 1$	-3
0	$(0)^2 + 3(0) - 1$	-1
1	$(1)^2 + 3(1) - 1$	3
2	$(2)^2 + 3(2) - 1$	9

The ordered pairs are:

$(-5, 9), (-4, 3), (-3, -1), (-2, -3), (-1, -3), (0, -1), (1, 3)$ and $(2, 9)$.

Plot these points and join them up to graph the function $f(x)$.

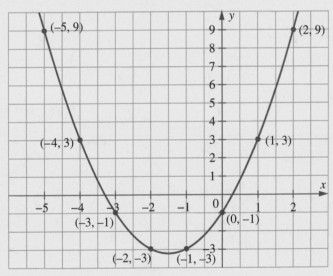

Alternative method to finding the points:

$f(-5) = (-5)^2 + 3(-5) - 1 = 9$ $\qquad$ $f(-1) = (-1)^2 + 3(-1) - 1 = -3$

$f(-4) = (-4)^2 + 3(-4) - 1 = 3$ $\qquad$ $f(0) = (0)^2 + 3(0) - 1 = -1$

$f(-3) = (-3)^2 + 3(-3) - 1 = -1$ $\qquad$ $f(1) = (1)^2 + 3(1) - 1 = 3$

$f(-2) = (-2)^2 + 3(-2) - 1 = -3$ $\qquad$ $f(2) = (2)^2 + 3(2) - 1 = 9$

The ordered pairs are: $(-5, 9), (-4, 3), (-3, -1), (-2, -3), (-1, -3), (0, -1),$
$(1, 3)$ and $(2, 9)$.

The Table mode on the Casio calculator can be used to verify the outputs of a function. You can input the function and the domain of inputs and then the calculator will give all outputs. It's a good idea to practise this function on your calculator to become familiar with it.

(i) Three functions $f(x)$, $g(x)$ and $h(x)$ are defined as follows:

$$f(x) = 2x^2 + x - 6 \qquad g(x) = x^2 - 6x + 9 \qquad h(x) = x^2 - 2x$$

(a) Solve $f(x) = 0$. **(b)** Solve $g(x) = 0$. **(c)** Solve $h(x) = 0$.

(ii) The table below shows the sketches of six different functions. Three of the sketches belong to the three functions from part **(i)**.

Identify which sketch represents which of the functions $f(x)$, $g(x)$ or $h(x)$.

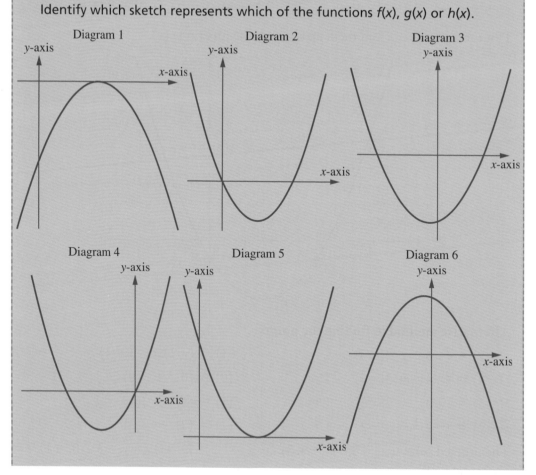

Solution

(i) (a) $f(x) = 2x^2 + x - 6$

$0 = 2x^2 + x - 6$

$0 = (2x - 3)(x + 2)$

$x = \dfrac{3}{2}$ or $x = -2$

(b) $g(x) = x^2 - 6x + 9$

$0 = x^2 - 6x + 9$

$0 = (x - 3)(x - 3)$

$x = 3$ or $x = 3$

(c) $h(x) = x^2 - 2x$

$0 = x^2 - 2x$

$0 = x(x - 2)$

$0 = x$ or $x = 2$

(ii) Each function starts with a positive x^2 term, so we can immediately dismiss diagrams 1 and 6 because these are ∩-shaped. The roots of the function, found in part **(i)**, are the points where the functions cross the x-axis.

- $f(x)$ has one negative root and one positive root. Therefore, $f(x)$ is diagram 3.
- $g(x)$ has two equal roots, so the minimum point on the curve is touching the x-axis. Therefore, $g(x)$ is diagram 5.
- $h(x)$ has roots 0 and 2, so it passes through the origin. Therefore, $h(x)$ is diagram 2.

Example

Shown below is the graph of the function $f : x \rightarrow 3 + 2x - x^2$
in the domain $-2 \leq x \leq 4$.
Use the graph to find:

(i) The values of x for which $f(x) = 0$

(ii) The values of x for which $f(x) = 3$

(iii) The values of x for which $f(x) = -5$

(iv) The value of $f(1)$

(v) Estimate the value of $f(3 \cdot 5)$

(vi) The coordinates of the maximum point

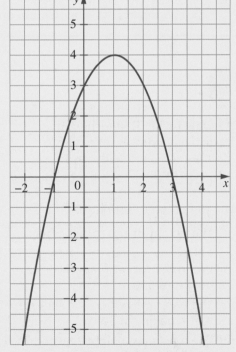

Solution

(i) To find the values of x for which $f(x) = 0$ means to find the values of x when $y = 0$. Go to 0 on the y-axis and move across horizontally in both directions until you hit the graph. You hit the graph at $x = -1$ and $x = 3$. **Therefore, when $f(x) = 0$, $x = -1$ and 3.**

(ii) To find the values of x for which $f(x) = 3$ means to find the values of x when $y = 3$. Go to 3 on the y-axis and move across horizontally in both directions until you hit the graph. You hit the graph at $x = 0$ and $x = 2$. **Therefore, when $f(x) = 3$, $x = 0$ and 2.**

(iii) To find the values of x for which $f(x) = -5$ means to find the values of x when $y = -5$. Go to -5 on the y-axis and move across horizontally in both directions until you hit the graph. You hit the graph at $x = -2$ and $x = 4$. **Therefore, when $f(x) = -5$, $x = -2$ and 4.**

(iv) To find the value of $f(1)$ means to find the value of y when $x = 1$. Go to 1 on the x-axis and move vertically until you hit the graph. You hit the graph at $y = 4$. **Therefore, $f(1) = 4$.**

(v) To find the values of $f(3 \cdot 5)$ means to find the values of y when $x = 3 \cdot 5$. Go to $3 \cdot 5$ on the x-axis and move vertically until you hit the graph. You hit the graph at $y = -2 \cdot 2$. **Therefore, $f(3 \cdot 5) = -2 \cdot 2$.**

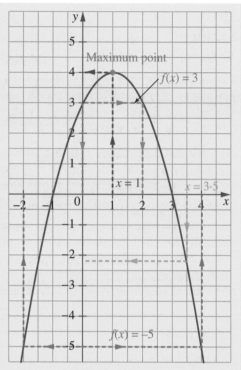

(vi) The maximum point it the highest point that the curve reaches. For this function, the coordinates of the **maximum point are $(1, 4)$.**

A model rocket is launched. Its height, h, in metres, t seconds after launch is modelled by $h(t) = -16t^2 + 200t + 2$.

Use the graph to estimate:

(i) The height of the rocket after 2 seconds

(ii) When the rocket first reaches a height of 550 m

(iii) The two times when the rocket is at a height of 300 m

(iv) The maximum height reached by the rocket

(v) For how long the rocket is above a height of 150 m

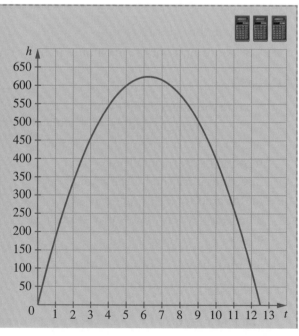

Solution

(i) To find h when $t = 2$:

Go to 2 on the t-axis, draw a line vertically upwards (green line) until you hit the graph, then draw a line horizontally across to read the value for h at this point. Estimate when $t = 2$, $h = 340$ m.

(ii) To find t when $h = 550$ m:

Go to 550 on the h-axis, draw a line horizontally across (blue line) until you hit the graph, then draw a line vertically downwards to read the value for t at this point. Estimate when $h = 550$, $t = 4$ sec.

(iii) To find two values for t when $h = 300$ m:

Go to 300 on the h-axis, draw a line horizontally across (purple line) until you hit the graph, then draw a line vertically downwards to read the value for t at these points. Estimate when $h = 300$, $t = 1\cdot7$ sec and $10\cdot8$ sec.

(iv) To find maximum height, draw a line horizontally across from the top of the curve (red line) to read the value for h at this point. Estimate $h = 630$ m at maximum height.

(v) To find two values for t when $h = 150$ m:

Go to 150 on the h-axis, draw a line horizontally across (yellow line) until you hit the graph, then draw a line vertically downwards to read the value for t at these points. Estimate when $h = 150$, $t = 0\cdot75$ sec and $11\cdot75$ sec. Therefore, the rocket is above 150 m for between $11\cdot75 - 0\cdot75 = 11$ seconds.

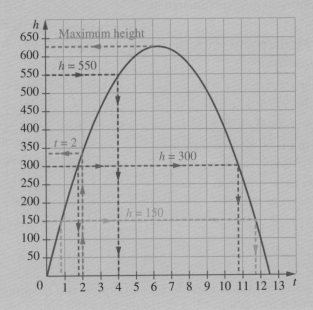

Example

Let f be the function $f: x \to 5 - 3x - 2x^2$ and g be the function $g: x \to -2x - 1$.

(i) Using the same axes and scales, draw the graph of f and the graph of g for $-3 \leq x \leq 2, x \in \mathbb{R}$.

Use your graphs from part (i) to estimate:

(ii) The maximum value of $f(x)$

(iii) The values of x for which $f(x) = g(x)$

(iv) The range of values of x for which $f(x) \geq g(x)$

Solution

(i)

x	$5 - 3x - 2x^2$	$f(x)$
-3	$5 - 3(-3) - 2(-3)^2$	-4
-2	$5 - 3(-2) - 2(-2)^2$	3
-1	$5 - 3(-1) - 2(-1)^2$	6
0	$5 - 3(0) - 2(0)^2$	5
1	$5 - 3(1) - 2(1)^2$	0
2	$5 - 3(2) - 2(2)^2$	-9

x	$-2x - 1$	$g(x)$
-3	$-2(-3) - 1$	5
-2	$-2(-2) - 1$	3
-1	$-2(-1) - 1$	1
0	$-2(0) - 1$	-1
1	$-2(1) - 1$	-3
2	$-2(2) - 1$	-5

Graphing the points:

(ii) Maximum point on $f(x)$ is estimated as $(-0.7, 6.1)$.

(iii) $f(x) = g(x)$ at the points where the two graphs overlap.

This occurs when $x = -2$ and $x = 1.5$.

(iv) Range of values for $f(x) \geq g(x)$:

This means to find the values of x for which the $f(x)$ graph is greater than (higher than) the $g(x)$ graph. This occurs for $-2 \leq x \leq 1.5$.

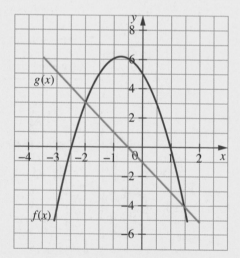

key point

Majority of marks are usually awarded for the table and graphing the function. Take care to work out the coordinates of the points correctly.

The diagram below shows part of the graphs of the functions
$f(x) = x^2 - 4x + 3$ and $g(x) = x + k$.

The graph of $f(x)$ cuts the x-axis at A and B.

The graphs of $f(x)$ and $g(x)$ intersect at A.

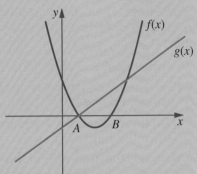

(i) Find the coordinates of A and the
coordinates of B.

(ii) Find the value of k.

(iii) Verify that $f(x)$ and $g(x)$ intersect also at the
point (4, 3).

Solution

(i) The points A and B are the points where the function crosses the x-axis. Their
x-coordinates are the solutions (the roots) of the quadratic equation $f(x) = 0$:

$$f(x) = x^2 - 4x + 3$$
$$x^2 - 4x + 3 = 0$$
$$(x - 3)(x - 1) = 0$$
$$x = 3 \quad \text{or} \quad x = 1$$

Therefore, $A = (1, 0)$ and $B = (3, 0)$.

(ii) The point $A = (1, 0)$ is on $g(x)$:

$$g(x) = x + k$$
$$y = x + k$$
$$0 = 1 + k$$
$$-1 = k$$

(iii) The two functions are:

$$y = x^2 - 4x + 3 \quad \text{and} \quad y = x - 1$$

To find points of intersection: let $y = y$.

$$x^2 - 4x + 3 = x - 1$$
$$x^2 - 5x + 4 = 0$$
$$(x - 4)(x - 1) = 0$$
$$x - 4 = 0 \quad \text{or} \quad x - 1 = 0$$
$$x = 4 \quad \text{or} \quad x = 1$$
$$y = x - 1$$
$$y = 4 - 1$$
$$y = 3$$

Point is (4, 3) as required.

The function $f(x) = x^2 + bx + c$ is graphed on the right. The curve contains the point $(-3, -4)$ and it crosses the x-axis at the point $(1, 0)$.

(i) Write down two equations in b and c.

(ii) Solve these equations to find the values of b and c.

(iii) Use these values for b and c to write down the function $f(x)$.

(iv) Use this function to find the coordinates of the points P and Q.

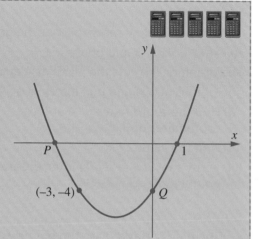

Solution

(i) Point $(1, 0)$ is on the function.

This means when $x = 1$, $y = 0$:

$$y = x^2 + bx + c$$
$$0 = (1)^2 + b(1) + c$$
$$0 = 1 + b + c$$
$$-1 = b + c \qquad ①$$

Point $(-3, -4)$ is on the function.

This means when $x = -3$, $y = -4$:

$$y = x^2 + bx + c$$
$$-4 = (-3)^2 + b(-3) + c$$
$$-4 = 9 - 3b + c$$
$$-13 = -3b + c \qquad ②$$

> **exam focus**
>
> If a point is on the graph of a function, you can substitute its coordinates into the function.

(ii) Solving simultaneously:

$$
\begin{array}{ll}
① & b + c = -1 \\
② & -3b + c = -13 \qquad (x - 1) \\
\hline
& b + c = -1 \\
& 3b - c = 13 \\
\hline
& 4b = 12 \\
& b = 3
\end{array}
$$

Let $b = 3$:
$$b + c = -1$$
$$3 + c = -1$$
$$c = -1 - 3$$
$$c = -4$$

(iii) $f(x) = x^2 + bx + c \qquad (b = 3 \text{ and } c = -4)$

$\therefore f(x) = x^2 + 3x - 4$

(iv) At x-axis, $y = 0$.

$$y = x^2 + 3x - 4$$
$$0 = x^2 + 3x - 4$$
$$0 = (x + 4)(x - 1)$$
$$x + 4 = 0 \quad \text{or} \quad x - 1 = 0$$

Crosses x-axis at $(-4, 0)$ and $(1, 0)$.

Therefore, point $P = (-4, 0)$.

At y-axis, $x = 0$.

$$y = x^2 + 3x - 4$$
$$y = (0)^2 + 3(0) - 4$$
$$y = -4$$

Therefore, point $Q = (0, -4)$.

The perimeter of a rectangle is 14 cm. The width of the rectangle is x cm.

(i) Write an expression, in terms of x, for the length of the rectangle.

(ii) Show that the area of the rectangle, in cm^2, is given by $7x - x^2$.

(iii) Let f be the function $f: x \rightarrow 7x - x^2$. Draw the graph of f for $0 \geq x \geq 7$, $x \in \mathbb{R}$.

(iv) Use your graph from part **(iii)** to estimate:

(a) The area of the rectangle when the width is 1·5 cm.

(b) The maximum possible area of the rectangle

(c) The two possible values of the width of the rectangle when the area is 4 cm^2

Solution

(i)
$$\text{Perimeter} = 14$$
$$2(\text{Length}) + 2(\text{Width}) = 14 \quad \text{(divide both sides by 2)}$$
$$\text{Length} + \text{Width} = 7$$
$$\text{Length} + x = 7$$
$$\text{Length} = 7 - x$$

(ii) Area = (Length)(Width)

Area = $(7 - x)(x)$

Area = $7x - x^2$

(iii)

x	$7x - x^2$	Area
0	$7(0) - (0)^2$	0
1	$7(1) - (1)^2$	6
2	$7(2) - (2)^2$	10
3	$7(3) - (3)^2$	12
4	$7(4) - (4)^2$	12
5	$7(5) - (5)^2$	10
6	$7(6) - (6)^2$	6
7	$7(7) - (7)^2$	0

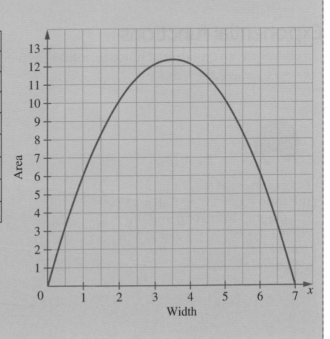

(iv) (a) To find the area when the width is 1·5 cm, go to 1·5 on the *x*-axis and find the corresponding value on the area axis (red line on graph). Area = 8·25 cm².

(b) Maximum area is at the highest point on the graph. Max. area = 12·25 cm².

(c) Find width when area = 4. Go to 4 on the area axis and go horizontally across to the graph (yellow line). At the two points where the line hits the graph, drop down vertically.

The two values for width which give an area of 4 cm² are 0·6 cm and 6·4 cm.

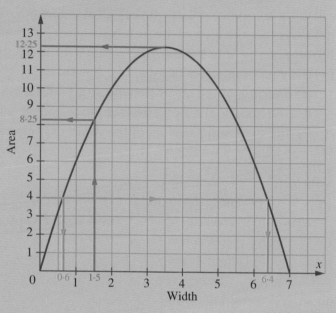

Exponential functions

On our course, an exponential function will be given in the form $f : x \rightarrow a2^x$ or $f : x \rightarrow a3^x$, where $a \in \mathbb{N}$ and $x \in \mathbb{R}$.

key point

For exponential graphs in the form $f(x) = a2^x$ or $f(x) = a3^x$, the graph is increasing and the curve intersects the *y*-axis at the point (0, *a*). This point is called the focal point.

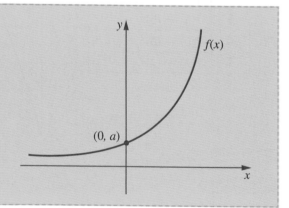

Example

The function, f, is defined as $f : x \rightarrow 5(3^x)$.

(i) Graph the function f in the domain $-2 \leq x \leq 2$.

(ii) Use the graph to find the focal point for the graph.

(iii) Use the graph to estimate the value of x for which $f(x) = 30$.

Solution

(i)

x	$5(3^x)$	$f(x)$
-2	$5(3^{-2})$	$\dfrac{5}{9}$
-1	$5(3^{-1})$	$\dfrac{5}{3}$
0	$5(3^0)$	5
1	$5(3^1)$	15
2	$5(3^2)$	45

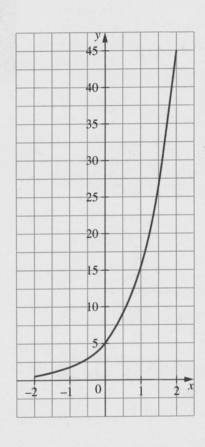

(ii) The focal point is the point where the graph crossed the y-axis. From the graph we can see the focal point is $(0, 5)$.

(iii) Go to 30 on the y-axis, go horizontally across to the graph and then drop a vertical line down to find the corresponding value of x.

When $f(x) = 30, x = 1 \cdot 6$.

The number of bacteria, $B(t)$, in a sample after t hours can be represented by the model: $B(t) = 50(2^t)$.

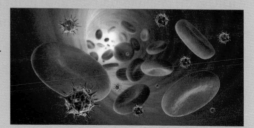

(i) Graph the number of bacteria for the first 5 hours.

(ii) Use the graph to estimate the number of bacteria present after 4·5 hours.

(iii) Use the graph to estimate after how many hours there are 600 bacteria present in the sample.

Solution

(i)

t	$50(2^t)$	$B(t)$
0	$50(2^0)$	50
1	$50(2^1)$	100
2	$50(2^2)$	200
3	$50(2^3)$	400
4	$50(2^4)$	800
5	$50(2^5)$	1 600

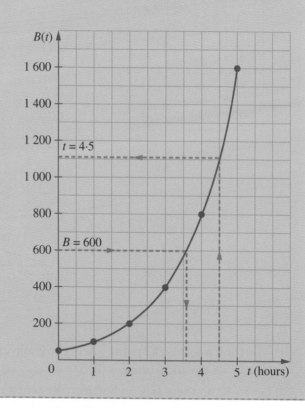

(ii) From the graph:
when $t = 4\cdot5$ hours,
$B(4\cdot5) = 1\,120$
(red line).

(iii) From the graph:
when $B = 600$, $T = 3\cdot6$
hours
(green line).

Match the following eight graphs to the eight functions.
Give a reason for your answer in each case.

A

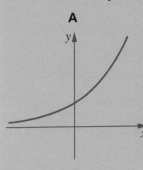

B

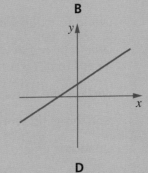

Functions

1. $y = x^2 - 8x + 16$

2. $y = 3$

3. $y = -3x + 2$

4. $y = x^2 - 7x + 10$

5. $x = -2$

6. $y = 2x + 5$

7. $y = -x^2 + x - 6$

8. $y = 3^x$

C

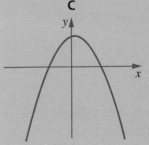

D

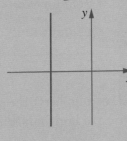

E

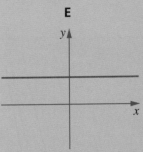

F

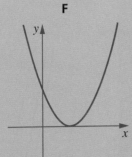

G

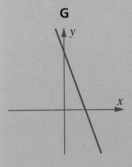

H

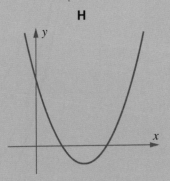

Solution

Graph	Function	Reason
A	8. $y = 3^x$	Exponential graph, moving upward
B	6. $y = 2x + 5$	Linear function with a positive slope
C	7. $y = -x^2 + x - 6$	Quadratic graph with a negative x^2 part means that it is a ∩-shaped graph
D	5. $x = -2$	Vertical line through the point $x = -2$
E	2. $y = 3$	Horizontal line through the point $y = 3$
F	1. $y = x^2 - 8x + 16$	Quadratic graph with equal roots
G	3. $y = -3x + 2$	Linear function with a negative slope
H	4. $y = x^2 - 7x + 10$	Quadratic function with two distinct roots

Transforming graphs

By adding and subtracting constant values (numbers), the position of a graph can be transformed (moved) in either the vertical or horizontal direction, or both.

Transforming graphs in the vertical direction (vertical shift):

Adding a constant to a function moves the graph of the function vertically **upwards** by that constant.

In the diagram, $f(x) + 2$ is two units above $f(x)$.

Subtracting a constant from a function moves the graph of the function vertically **downwards** by that constant.

In the diagram, $f(x) - 1$ is one unit below $f(x)$.

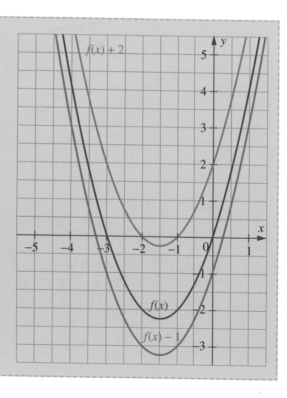

key point

Transforming graphs in the horizontal direction (horizontal shift):

Adding a **constant** to the x-part of a function moves the graph of the function horizontally to the **left** by that constant.

In the diagram, $f(x + 2)$ is two units to the left of $f(x)$.

Subtracting a **constant** from the x-part of a function moves the graph of the function horizontally to the **right** by that constant.

In the diagram, $f(x - 1)$ is one unit to the right of $f(x)$.

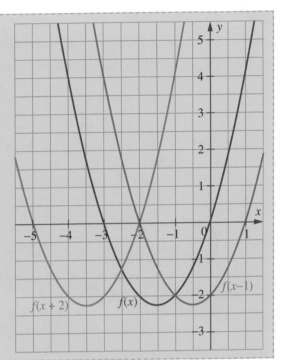

Example

(i) Graph the function $f : x \rightarrow 3^x$ in the domain $-1 \leq x \leq 2$.

(ii) On the same axis and scale, draw the graph of the function $h : x \rightarrow f(x) - 10$.

Solution

(i)

x	3^x	y
-1	3^{-1}	$0 \cdot 33$
0	3^0	1
1	3^1	3
2	3^2	9

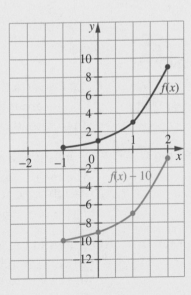

Ordered pairs:
$(-1, 0 \cdot 33), (0, 1), (1, 3)$ and $(2, 9)$.
Graph these points to get $f(x)$ (in blue).

(ii) $h : x \rightarrow f(x) - 10$ means that the function $h(x)$ equals $f(x)$ minus 10.

The result of this is that the graph of $h(x)$ is the same shape as $f(x)$, but it is 10 units directly below the graph of $f(x)$.

Therefore, the points on $h(x)$ are: $(-1, -9 \cdot 67), (0, -9), (1, -7)$ and $(2, -1)$

Graph these points to get $h(x)$ (in red).

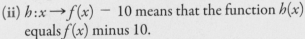

The function A (blue) is defined by the equation $y = x^2$.
By observation, or otherwise, write down the equation of the functions B, C and D.

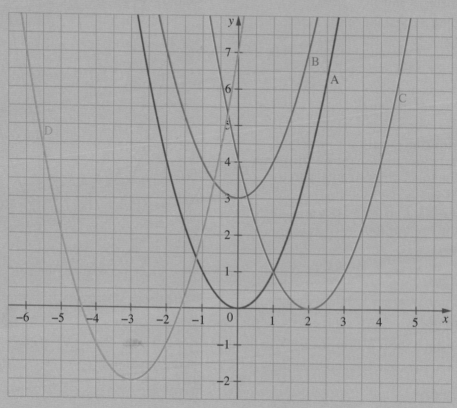

Solution

Graph B: 3 units vertically above graph A.

This means that we must add 3 to the equation for graph A.

Therefore, the equation of B: $y = x^2 + 3$.

Graph C: 2 units to the right of graph A.

This means that the equation of C is the same as A, but with 2 subtracted from the x part.

Therefore, the equation of C: $y = (x - 2)^2$.

Graph D: 3 units to the left of A **and** 2 units below A.

This means that we must add 3 to the **x** part **and** subtract 2 from the overall function.

Therefore, the equation of D: $y = (x + 3)^2 - 2$.

A group of four students is studying graphs of functions of the form $f: x \rightarrow x^2 + 2x + k$, $x \in \mathbb{R}$. Each takes an integer value of k and draws the graph of their function in a suitable domain. Maria took $k = -8$ and drew the graph below.

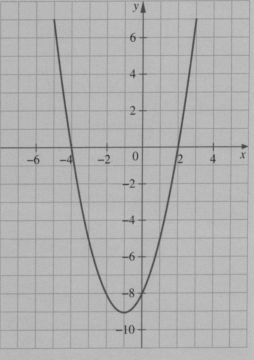

(i) Use the graph to write down the roots of the equation $x^2 + 2x - 8 = 0$.

(ii) Keith's graph passes through the point (3, 2). Find the value of k that Keith used.

(iii) On Alice's graph, the two roots of the function are the same. Find the value of k that Alice used.

(iv) Draw a sketch of Alice's function on the diagram shown in part **(i)**.

(v) Emma's graph shows that the roots of her function are -5 and 3. Find the value of k that she used.

Solution

(i) From the diagram, the roots of $x^2 + 2x - 8 = 0$ are -4 and 2.

(ii) $f(x) = x^2 + 2x + k$ contains (3, 2).
Let $x = 3$ and $y = 2$:

$$y = x^2 + 2x + k$$

$$2 = (3)^2 + 2(3) + k$$

$$2 = 9 + 6 + k$$

$$2 = 15 + k$$

$$-13 = k$$

(iii) If the roots of Alice's function are equal, then the lowest point on her graph must be touching the x-axis. So we take Maria's function and move it upwards until the minimum point on the curve is touching the x-axis. This is achieved by adding 9 onto Maria's function.

Therefore, Alice's function $= (x^2 + 2x - 8) + 9 = x^2 + 2x + 1$.

This means that $k = 1$

(iv) Graphing Alice's function alongside Maria's function gives:

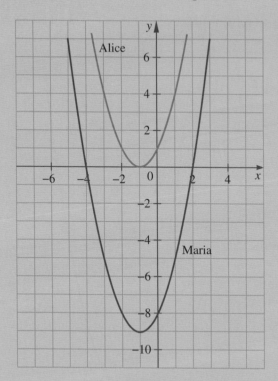

(v) If Emma's function has roots of −5 and 3:

$$x = -5 \text{ or } x = 3$$

$$(x + 5)(x - 3) = 0$$

$$x^2 - 3x + 5x - 15 = 0$$

$$x^2 + 2x - 15 = 0$$

Therefore, Emma let $k = -15$.

key
point

The method of forming a quadratic equation when given the roots of the equation was covered in an earlier chapter.

15 Rounding, Estimates, Ratio, Direct Proportion and Graphs

aims

- ☐ To be able to present numerical answers to degree of accuracy specified.
- ☐ To be able to make approximations and estimates of calculations.
- ☐ To learn how to use ratio and proportion.
- ☐ To draw and interpret graphs of direct proportion.

Rounding

In the exam we are sometimes asked to round our answers.

The number 9·4837 = 9 correct to the nearest whole number
= 9·5 correct to one decimal place
= 9·48 correct to two decimal places
= 9·484 correct to three decimal places

The number 68 176 = 70 000 correct to one significant figure
= 68 000 correct to two significant figures
= 68 200 correct to three significant figures

key point

When expressing a whole number correct to a given number of significant figures, zeros at the end of the number are not counted but must be included in the final result. All other zeros are significant, e.g 90 426 = 90 400 correct to three significant figures.

Changing units in the metric system

We are often required to change from one unit to another, as illustrated in the following exam question.

exam focus

The booklet of formulae and tables may help.

(i) Change 5 000 g to kilograms.

(ii) Change 2·7 m to centimetres.

(iii) Change 8 000 cm³ to litres.

(iv) Change 4 m² to cm².

Solution

(i) $5\ 000\ g = \dfrac{5\ 000}{1\ 000} = 5\ kg$

(ii) $2\cdot7\ m = 2\cdot7 \times 100 = 270\ cm$

or $2\cdot7\ m = \dfrac{2\cdot7}{\frac{1}{100}} = 2\cdot7 \times \dfrac{100}{1} = 270\ cm$

(iii) $8\ 000\ cm^3 = \dfrac{8\ 000}{1\ 000} = 8\ell,$

(iv) $1\ m = 100\ cm \Rightarrow 1\ m^2 = 100 \times 100\ cm^2$

$4\ m^2 = 4 \times 100 \times 100\ cm^2 = 40\ 000\ cm^2$

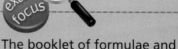

The booklet of formulae and tables, gives us:

$Kilo = 10^3\ (= 1\ 000)$

$Centi = 10^{-2}\left(= \dfrac{1}{100}\right)$

key point

$1\ell, = 1\ 000\ cm^3$

You must know this.

Estimates

There are many occasions when it is either desirable or necessary to round off large or small numbers to a reasonable degree of accuracy.

With the widespread use of calculators, it is important that we have some estimate of the answer we expect to get. Then we will know whether the answer shown on the calculator is reasonable or not.

Jack had to estimate the cost of 396 teddy bears. The calculation he used was $396 \times 27\cdot25$.

Without a calculator, Jack has to estimate the answer.

396 is approximately 400

27·25 is approximately 27

Hence, an approximate answer is $400 \times 27 = €10\ 800$

Croke Park in Dublin holds 82 300 people when full.

During a football match a reporter estimated that the stadium was 40% full.

How many people were estimated to be at the game?

Give your answer correct to the nearest 100 people.

Solution

$$100\% = 82\ 300$$

$$1\% = \frac{82\ 300}{100} = 823$$

$$40\% = 823 \times 40 = 32\ 920$$

Alternatively,

40% of the stadium = 82 300 × 0·40 = 32 920.

Then to the nearest 100 people we write 32 900.

(i) Karen went to a shop to buy five magazines. She had €10 to spend. She made an estimate of the total cost by correcting the price of each magazine to the next highest euro. The magazines cost €1·95, €1·99, €3·59, €1·40 and 99 cent. Work out her estimate.

(ii) Based on the estimate, would she think she had enough money?

(iii) Work out the exact cost of the magazines.

(iv) Suggest what you think is a better method for estimating the total cost of the magazines. Give a reason for your answer.

Solution

(i) €1·95 → 2·00

   €1·99 → 2·00

   €3·59 → 4·00

   €1·40 → 2·00

   €0·99 → 1·00

   Total = €11·00

(ii) Since her estimate is €11 and she has €10 to spend, she concludes she does not have enough money.

(iii) 1·95 + 1·99 + 3·59 + 1·40 + 0·99 = €9·92

(iv) It would be more accurate if Karen rounded to the nearest whole number.

This is likely to give a better estimate, as some prices will round up and some will round down.

Ratio

A ratio is a comparison between two similar quantities measured in the same units. It is written in a given order.

The ratio 11 to 4 is written 11:4 or as a fraction $\dfrac{11}{4}$.

Simplifying ratios

A ratio is unchanged if we multiply or divide each part by the same number, e.g. 11:4 is the same as $5\frac{1}{2}$:2.

It is usual to make each part of the ratio as small as possible. However, each part should be a whole number.

Example

€5 580 is shared between Fred and Ciara in the ratio of their ages. Fred is three times as old as Ciara.

(i) Write down the ratio of their ages.

(ii) How much money does each receive?

(iii) How much money would Fred have to give to Ciara so that they would have equal amounts?

Solution

(i) Fred:Ciara = 3:1

(ii) 3 + 1 = 4 is the total number of parts.

$1 \text{ part} = \dfrac{5\,580}{4} = €1\,395$, hence 3 parts $= 1\,395 \times 3 = €4\,185$

Ciara gets €1 395 and Fred gets €4 185.

(iii)

For both to have equal parts, the calculation is $\dfrac{5\,580}{2} = €2\,790$.

Hence, for Fred and Ciara to have equal amounts, Fred must give Ciara 4 185 − 2 790 = €1 395.

Millie bakes cakes and sells them at the local market.

(i) Millie needs 4 eggs to make each cake. She has 28 eggs. How many cakes can she make?

(ii) Millie makes a filling for her cakes using only butter and sugar. The ratio of the weight of butter to sugar is 5 : 7. One day, Millie makes a total of 2·4 kg of filling. Work out how many grams of sugar Millie used to make this filling.

(iii) Millie is buying flour at her local shop. The shop has two special offers. Millie wants to buy 6 kg of flour. Work out which offer, A or B, will give her the better value.

Special Offer A	Special Offer B
1 kg bags: €3·50 each	1·5 kg bags: €5 each
Special offer:	Special offer:
3 bags for the price of 2	20% off

Better value: **offer A**   **offer B**

(tick (✓) **one** box only) ☐   ☐

(iv) Millie sells each cake for €7·50. This gives her a profit of 20%. Work out how much it costs Millie to make each cake.

Solution

(i) 4 eggs make 1 cake.
28 eggs contain 7 groups of 4, so Millie can make 7 cakes using the 28 eggs.

(ii) Divide 2·4 kg in the ratio 5 : 7.

Add the ratios: $5 + 7 = 12$ parts

Divide 2·4 kg by 12 to find 1 part: 1 part $= \dfrac{2·4 \text{ kg}}{12} = \dfrac{2\,400 \text{ g}}{12} = 200$ g

The sugar portion is 7 parts: $200 \text{ g} \times 7 = 1\,400$ g

(iii) *Special offer A*
To buy 6 kg, Millie will need six bags of flour.

The offer is 3 bags for the price of 2, so she will only pay for 4 bags of flour.

Cost $= 4 \times$ €3·50 $=$ €14

Special offer B

To buy 6 kg, Millie will need $\dfrac{6}{1·5} = 4$ bags

Cost $= 4 \times$ €5 $=$ €20
Discount $= 20\%$ of €20 $=$ €4
Cost after discount $=$ €20 $-$ €4 $=$ €16

€14 is less than €16, therefore, we can see that offer A is better:

         offer A   **offer B**

           ✓☑   ☐

(iv) Selling price (including profit of 20%):   €7·50 $= 120\%$

Divide both sides by 120:   €0·0625 $= 1\%$

Cost price (before the profit of 20%):   €6·25 $= 100\%$

So it costs Millie €6·25 to make each cake.

A soccer team has three strikers, John, Paul and Michael. The number of minutes each had played by the end of a particular season is shown on the table. The team divided a bonus of €150 000 between its strikers in proportion to the time each had played.

Name	Minutes Played
John	2 250
Paul	2 600
Michael	150

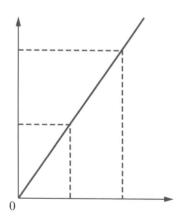

Calculate the amount each player received.

Solution

2 250 + 2 600 + 150 = 5 000 shares

1 share is worth $\dfrac{\text{bonus}}{5\ 000} = \dfrac{150\ 000}{5\ 000} = €30$

That represents a bonus of €30 per minute played.

John gets 2 250 × 30 = €67 500.

Paul gets 2 600 × 30 = €78 000.

Michael gets 150 × 30 = €4 500.

Directly proportional graphs

If a graph of two variables is a straight line through the origin, then one variable is **directly proportional** to the other. This means that if one variable changes, then the other also changes by the same ratio.

Example

Noah is filling this cylinder with water. The water is being delivered from the tap at the rate of 120 ml/sec.

Noah times how long it takes to fill the cylinder.

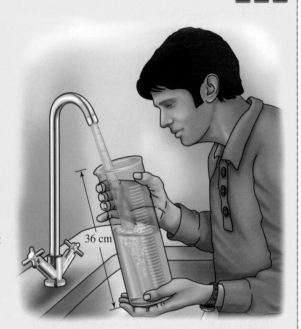

Height of water (cm)	6	12	18	24	30	36
Time taken (sec)	1·2	2·4	3·6	4·8	6·0	7·2

(i) Draw a graph of height against time.

(ii) Use your graph to find the height of the water after 5 seconds.

(iii) How long does it take for the water to reach a height of 20 cm?

Solution

(i)

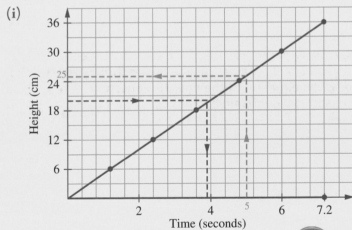

(ii) From the graph after 5 seconds the height is 25 cm.

(iii) From the graph a height of 20 cm is reached after 3·9 seconds.

exam focus

Occasionally a question includes information that is not required for a successful solution. In this case, 'the rate of 120 ml/sec' is not required.

Example

The previous question based on Noah filling the cylinder with water may be presented in the following way:

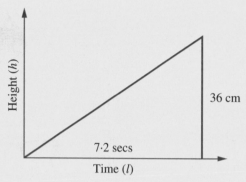

Use the gradient of the graph to find the rule connecting the two variables.

Solution

The gradient = The slope $= m = \dfrac{\text{Rise}}{\text{Run}} = \dfrac{36}{7{\cdot}2} = \dfrac{360}{72} = 5$

This tells us that a slope of 5 represents an increase of 5 cm in height every second.

The above question may link with the formula $y = mx + c$ from Coordinate Geometry, where $m = 5$ and $c = 0$ because the line passes through the origin. Hence, we write $y = 5x$ as the equation of the line. This question is an example of where the examiner could unify strands.

exam
Q

In which of these graphs is q directly proportional to t?

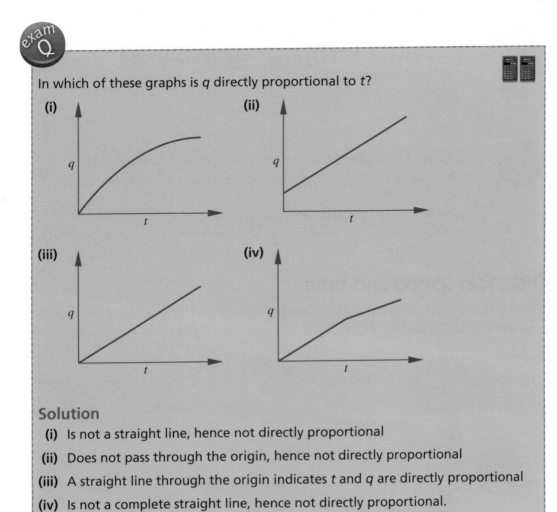

Solution

(i) Is not a straight line, hence not directly proportional

(ii) Does not pass through the origin, hence not directly proportional

(iii) A straight line through the origin indicates t and q are directly proportional

(iv) Is not a complete straight line, hence not directly proportional.

16 Distance, Speed, Time and Graphs of Motion

- ☐ To learn how to solve problems involving distance, speed and time.
- ☐ To be able to apply your knowledge and skills to solve problems on graphs of motion.
- ☐ To be able to tell the story of a graph of motion.

Distance, speed and time

There are three formulae to remember when dealing with problems involving distance (D), speed (S) and time (T). (Note: Speed here means average speed.)

1. Speed $= \dfrac{\text{Distance}}{\text{Time}}$ **2.** Time $= \dfrac{\text{Distance}}{\text{Speed}}$ **3.** Distance = Speed × Time

It can be difficult to remember these formulae. To help you remember, consider the triangle on the right. By covering the quantity required (*D, S* or *T*), any of the three formulae above can be found by inspection.

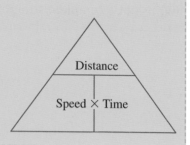

Common units of speed

1. Kilometres per hour, written as km/h
2. Metres per second, written as m/s

Marks may be lost if you do not include units in your answers, where appropriate.

A note on hours and minutes:

$$12 \text{ minutes} = \frac{12}{60} = 0\cdot2 \text{ hours}$$

$$30 \text{ minutes} = \frac{30}{60} = 0\cdot5 \text{ hours}$$

$$\frac{1}{3} \text{ hour} = \frac{1}{3} \times 60 = 20 \text{ minutes}$$

key point
- To convert minutes to hours divide by 60.
- To convert hours to minutes multiply by 60.

Example

An athlete ran 1 500 m in 4 minutes. Find the average speed of the athlete in

(i) metres per second   (ii) km per hour.

Solution

(i) $\text{Average speed} = \dfrac{\text{Distance travelled}}{\text{Time taken}} = \dfrac{1\,500}{4} = 375 \text{ m per minute}$

key point

1 minute = 60 seconds

$$375 \text{ m per minute} = 375 \text{ m per 60 seconds}$$
$$= \frac{375}{60} \text{ m per second}$$
$$= 6\cdot25 \text{ m per second}$$

(ii) $6\cdot25 \text{ m per second} = 6\cdot25 \times 60 \times 60 \text{ m per hour}$
$$= 22\,500 \text{ m per hour}$$
$$= \frac{22\,500}{1\,000} \text{ km per hour}$$
$$= 22\cdot5 \text{ km per hour}$$

key point

60 × 60 seconds
= 1 hour

and

1 000 m = 1 km

Example

A military aircraft travels at a speed of 900 metres per second for 2·5 minutes. Express the distance travelled in km.

Solution

$$\text{Distance travelled} = \text{Average speed} \times \text{Time taken}$$
$$= 900 \times 150$$
$$= 135\,000 \text{ m}$$
$$= \frac{135\,000}{1\,000} \text{ km}$$
$$= 135 \text{ km}$$

key point

2·5 minutes = 2·5 × 60 = 150 seconds

A man travels from Blanchardstown to Cootehill, a distance of 112 km. He leaves Blanchardstown at 10:55, travelling at an average speed of 64 km per hour. At what time does he arrive in Cootehill?

Solution

$$\text{Time taken} = \frac{\text{Distance travelled}}{\text{Average speed}} = \frac{112}{64} = 1\cdot75 \text{ hours} = 1 \text{ hour } 45 \text{ minutes}$$

key point

1·75 hours = 1 hour 45 minutes and **not** 1 hour 75 minutes

Hence   10:55
   +   1:45
   ─────────
      11:100   = 12:40 is the arrival time

Light travels at a speed of approximately (2.9×10^5) km/sec. How many kilometres will light travel in 8 minutes?

Express your answer in the form $a \times 10^n$, where $n \in \mathbb{N}$ and $1 \leq a < 10$.

key point

$10^5 = 100\ 000$, hence $2.9 \times 10^5 = 290\ 000$.

Solution

Light travels at: 290 000 km/sec

$290\ 000 \times 60$ km in 1 minute

$290\ 000 \times 60 \times 8$ km in 8 minutes

$139\ 200\ 000$ km in 8 minutes

1.392×10^8 km in 8 minutes

exam focus

Be sure to know how to handle indices (powers).

Car A and Car B set off from a starting point, S, at the same time. They travel the same route to destination D, which is 70 km away. Car A travels at an average speed of 50 km/h and car B travels at an average speed of 45 km/h.

How far will car B have travelled by the time car A arrives at destination D?

S ●——————————————● D

Solution

Use Time $= \dfrac{\text{Distance}}{\text{Speed}}$ on car A (the faster car)

$\text{Time} = \dfrac{70}{50} = 1.4$ hours

Hence, car B distance travelled $= \text{Speed} \times \text{Time}$

$= 45 \times 1.4$

$= 63$ km

exam focus

This was a well-answered question worth 15 marks. 7 of those marks were awarded for any correct version of the time–distance–speed formula. Be sure to write down something for each part of each question.

Olive cycled to the shop to get some milk for her tea. She cycled along a particular route and returned by the same route. The graph below shows the different stages of her journey.

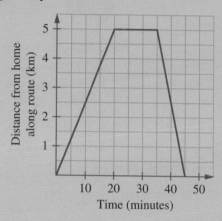

 (i) How long did Olive stay in the shop?

 (ii) How far from her home is the shop?

(iii) Compare the speed of her trip to the shop with her speed on the way home.

(iv) Write a paragraph to describe her journey.

Solution   (i) and (ii)

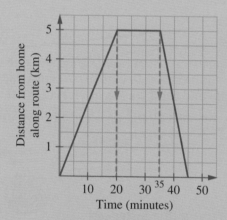

Reading from the graph, Olive stayed in the shop for $35 - 20 = 15$ minutes.

Reading from the graph, Olive's home is 5 km, or 5 000 m, from the shop.

(iii) Speed to the shop

$$= \frac{\text{Distance}}{\text{Time}}$$

$$= \frac{5\,000}{20}$$

$$= 250 \text{ m per minute}$$

Speed to her home

$$= \frac{\text{Distance}}{\text{Time}}$$

$$= \frac{5\,000}{10}$$

$$= 500 \text{ m per minute}$$

Comparing the two speeds we conclude Olive travelled home at twice the speed.

(iv) Olive cycled for 20 minutes at a speed of 250 m per minute on her way to the shop. She spent 15 minutes at the shop. On her return journey she cycled twice as fast and got home in 10 minutes.

Angela leaves home (*H*) at 5pm to go to football practice, which is 700 m away. The graph shows her journey, on foot, to football practice.

(i) One of the stories below matches Angela's journey. Place a tick in the box beside the correct matching story.

(Note: Only **one** story matches Angela's journey).

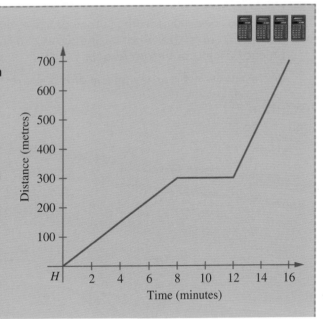

Story	Tick one story (✓)
P Angela walks at a constant pace and stops at 5:08 for 4 minutes. She then walks at a slower pace and arrives at practice at 5·16.	
Q Angela walks at a constant pace and stops at 5:12 for 4 minutes. She then walks at a faster pace and arrives at practice at 5·16.	
R Angela walks at a constant pace and stops at 5:08 for 5 minutes. She then walks at a faster pace and arrives at practice at 5·16.	
S Angela walks at a constant pace and stops at 5:08 for 4 minutes. She then walks at a faster pace and arrives at practice at 5·16.	
T Angela walks at a constant pace and stops at 5:08 for 4 minutes. She then walks at the same pace and arrives at practice at 5·16.	

(ii) Mary also lives 700 m from football practice, but cycles to practice. She leaves home 5 minutes after Angela. She cycles at a constant pace and arrives at practice 2 minutes before Angela.

Represent Mary's journey on the graph above.

Solution

(i)

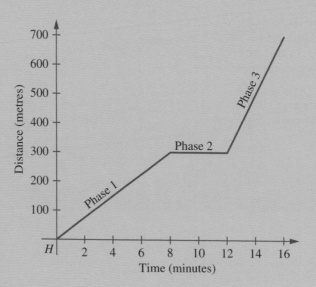

key point

There are three phase's to Angela's journey, as indicated on the graph.

In phase 1 she walks at a constant pace.
In phase 2 she stops a 5:08 for 4 minutes.
In phase 3 she walks at a faster pace.

The line representing phase 3 is the steepest line. The steeper the line, the faster she travels. This idea of steepness will appear in most travel graph exam questions.

Answer Box S ✓

(ii) Mary begins at the point (5, 0), as indicated. She continues (on the dotted line) to arrive 2 minutes before Angela.

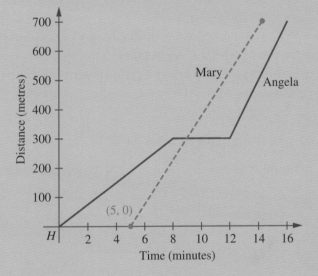

Part **(i)** was awarded 10 marks if the tick was in the correct box. It is vital you tick one and only one box. If you cannot figure it out, make your best guess and move on. Part **(ii)** was also awarded 10 marks. It was not well answered.

Most incorrect attempts, with some type of straight line, were awarded 5 marks.

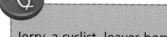

Jerry, a cyclist, leaves home at 10:00 a.m. and returns at 5:30 p.m. The distance he travels from home is shown on the graph below.

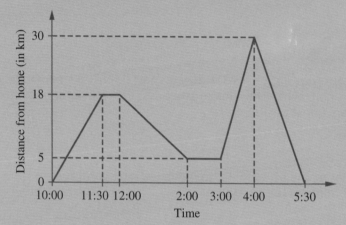

(i) Calculate his average speed between 10:00 a.m. and 11:30 a.m.

(ii) Calculate how far Jerry cycles during the day.

(iii) How many times during the day does he cycle towards his home?

(iv) What was his average speed for the whole day?

Solution

(i) Between 10:00 a.m. and 11:30 a.m. Jerry cycles 18 km.

$$\text{Average speed} = \frac{\text{Distance}}{\text{Time}} = \frac{18}{1\frac{1}{2}} = 12 \text{ km per hour}$$

In part (i) it is useful to observe that in the given graph

$$\text{Average speed} = \text{Gradient} = \text{Slope} = \frac{\text{Rise}}{\text{Run}}.$$

(ii) A summary of Jerry's journey

= phase 1 then rest, phase 2 then rest, phase 3 and phase 4

= 18 + 0 + (18 − 5) + 0 + (30 − 5) + 30

= 18 + 0 + 13 + 0 + 25 + 30

= 86 km

(iii)

In this case, distance from home increasing, then line ↗, means Jerry is moving away from home.

Distance from home decreasing, then line ↘, means Jerry is moving towards home.

Jerry cycles towards his home twice (once from 12:00 to 2:00 and the second time from 4:00 to 5:30).

(iv) Average speed $= \dfrac{\text{Total Distance}}{\text{Total Time}} = \dfrac{86}{7\frac{1}{2}} = \dfrac{86}{7\cdot5} = 11\cdot47$ km/hour

Example

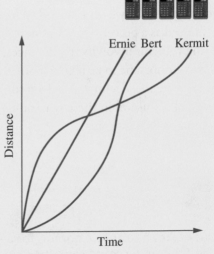

This graph shows the progress of three athletes, Bert, Kermit and Ernie, running an 800 m race.

(i) Describe separately the progress of each of the three athletes.

(ii) Describe the race.

Solution

(i) Ernie maintains the same speed for the total distance.
Bert starts slowly, increases his speed during the middle of the race and slows slightly at the end.
Kermit starts very fast, then slows down during the middle of the race. He quickens slightly at the end.

(ii) Kermit goes into the lead, followed by Ernie. Kermit begins to tire and is passed by Ernie. After halfway, Bert passes Kermit, but he cannot catch Ernie.

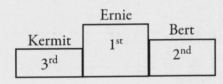

17 Arithmetic and Financial Maths

- ☐ To learn how to calculate household bills and VAT.
- ☐ To learn how to convert currencies/foreign exchange.
- ☐ To learn how to calculate percentage mark-up, margin and loss.
- ☐ To learn how to calculate compound interest and depreciation.
- ☐ To learn how to calculate income tax and other deductions.

Household bills and VAT

In this section we deal with household bills and VAT. Value-added tax (VAT) is a government tax which is added to many of the things that we buy. VAT is usually expressed as a percentage. When dealing with problems involving percentages, it is very important to be able to convert a percentage to a decimal. A calculator is particularly useful in these situations.

key point

To find 25%, multiply by 0·25.

To find 110%, multiply by 1·10.

To find 13·5%, multiply by 0·135.

exam Q

Jack takes his car to a garage for a service and receives an itemised bill. Find the total cost of servicing the car.

Itemised bill for service	Cost
5 litres of oil at €4·20 per litre	
2 windscreen wiper blades at €4·50 per blade	
2 brake shoes at €28 each	
2 hours of labour at €60 per hour	
Subtotal (before VAT added)	
VAT @ 13·5%	
Total bill	

Solution

€4·20 × 5 = €21·00 for oil

€4·50 × 2 = €9·00 for wiper blades

€28 × 2 = €56·00 for brake shoes

€60 × 2 = €120   for labour

        206·00 subtotal

         27·81 VAT @ 13·5%

    €233·81 total bill $\left[\text{given by } \frac{206}{100} \times 13\cdot5 = 27\cdot81 \right]$

The monthly line rental on Peter's mobile phone amounts to €12·70. During May, the duration of his calls is 1 hr 41 mins and 50 secs.

Calls are charged at 0·6 cent per second.

Calculate Peter's total bill for May.

Solution

1 hour = 60 mins = 60 × 60 secs =   3 600

        41 mins = 41 × 60 secs =   2 460

                 50 secs =   50

1 hour 41 mins and 50 seconds =   6 110 seconds

Cost 0·6 × 6 110 = 3 666 cents = €36·66

Total bill 12·70 + 36·66 = €49·36

Many candidates wrote 0·6 × 6 110 = €3 666! That's some phone bill!

Alex's gas bill gave the following data:

Unit type	Present reading	Previous reading	Unit price
Day rate	42 384	40 932	€0·1702
Night rate	16 528	15 791	€0·0951

(i) Calculate the total cost of the units used, to the nearest cent.

(ii) Alex also pays a standing charge of €28·12 and a levy of €6·38. VAT is charged on all amounts. If the total amount of Alex's gas bill is €429·10, find the rate of VAT, to the nearest whole number.

Solution

(i) Number of units used = Present reading – Previous reading

Day rate		Night rate	
Present reading:	42 384	Present reading:	16 528
Previous reading:	40 932	Previous reading:	15 791
	1 452 units		737 units
	× €0·1702		× €0·0951
Cost:	€247·1304	Cost:	€70·0887

Total cost of units: €247·1304 + €70·0887 = €317·2191 = €317·22

(ii) Charges:

Units:	€317·22
Standing charge:	€28·12
Levy:	€6·38
Total of charges:	€351·72

Total of bill = Total of charges + VAT

€429·10 = €351·72 + VAT

€77·38 = VAT

$$\text{Rate of VAT} = \frac{\text{VAT}}{\text{Total of charges}} \times 100$$

$$= \frac{€77·38}{€351·72} \times 100$$

$$= 22\%$$

Currency exchange

If we travel to a country not in the eurozone, we generally change our euro, €, to the currency of that country.

If you see €1 = 125 yen, ¥, displayed in a bank, how do you convert ¥10 000 to €?

We write ¥125 = €1

$$¥1 = €\frac{1}{125}$$

$$¥10\ 000 = €\frac{1}{125} \times 10\ 000 = €80$$

key point

Put the currency required on the right-hand side of the equation.

A hotel website gives the cost of staying for three nights in a hotel in Copenhagen as 2 925 Danish kroner.

(i) Find the cost in euro, given that €1 = 7·5 Danish kroner.

(ii) This cost includes a 5% service charge for the website company. Find, in euro, how much the hotel will get for the three-night stay. Give your answer to two decimal places.

Solution

(i)   7.5 Danish kroner = €1

$$1 \text{ Danish kroner} = €\frac{1}{7·5}$$

$$2\ 925 \text{ Danish kroner} = €\frac{1}{7·5} \times 2\ 925 = €390$$

Therefore, 2 925 kroner = €390.

(ii) The cost of €390 includes a 5% service charge.

105% = €390

1% = €3·714285

100% = €371·4285

Therefore, the hotel will receive €371·43.

The value of one euro against other currencies on a particular day is shown in the table below.

Currency	Rate (€)
US dollar	1·4045
Pound sterling	0·87315
Lithuanian litas	3·4528
Latvian lats	0·7093
Polish zloty	4·0440

(i) Mary was going to America for a few months. She changed €1 200 into US dollars using the exchange rate in the table.

   (a) How many dollars should she receive at this exchange rate?

   (b) The bank charged 3% commission on the transaction. How many dollars did she receive?

(ii) On returning to Ireland, Mary had $3 060. She changed this amount into euro. The bank again charged her 3% commission on the transaction. She received €2 047.

Find the exchange rate on that day, correct to two decimal places.

(iii) David changed a certain amount of sterling into euro at the exchange rate in the table above. A few days later he again changed the same amount of sterling into euro at a different exchange rate. He received fewer euro this time. No commission was charged on these transactions. Write down one possible value for the exchange rate for the second transaction.

This question was awarded a total of 30 marks.

Part **(i) (a)** was well answered and awarded 10 marks.

     (b) was well answered and awarded 10 marks.

  (ii) was badly answered and only awarded 5 marks.

  (iii) was very badly answered and awarded 5 marks.

As in the above exam question, it is often the case that most of the marks are awarded for the easier parts. Be mindful of this when in the exam and do not spend too much time on any one part of a question.

Solution

(i) (a)   €1 = $1·4045

    €1 200 = 1·4045 × 1 200 = $1 685·40

(b) 		$100\% = \$1\,685{\cdot}4$

$$1\% = \frac{1\,685{\cdot}4}{100}$$

$$\text{Commission} = 3\% = \frac{1\,685{\cdot}40 \times 3}{100} = \$50{\cdot}562$$

Mary received $1\,685{\cdot}4 - 50{\cdot}562 = \$1\,634{\cdot}838 = \$1\,634$

(ii) $100\% - 3\%$ commission $= 97\% = €2\,047$

$$1\% = \frac{2\,047}{97}$$

$$100\% = \frac{2\,047 \times 100}{97} = 2\,110{\cdot}309278$$

On the day $€2\,110{\cdot}309278 = \$3\,060$

Hence, the rate is $€1 = \dfrac{3\,060}{2\,110{\cdot}309278} = \$1{\cdot}45$

(iii) The rate for the first transaction was $€1 = £0{\cdot}87315$.

The second transaction results in $£0{\cdot}87315 < €1$.

This means the answer is any rate where $€1$ is worth more than $£0{\cdot}87315$.

Candidates were asked to *write down* one possible value. No explaination was required. Answers include:

$$€1 = £0{\cdot}90; \quad €1 = £0{\cdot}885, \text{ etc.}$$

Percentage profit and loss

When selling an item, the seller can make a profit if the selling price is greater than the cost price. Alternatively, the seller can make a loss if the selling price is less than the cost price.

The percentage profit can be measured as a percentage of the cost price (mark-up) or the selling price (margin). The percentage loss is measured as a percentage of the cost price. The formulae are as follows:

Mark-up	Margin	Percentage loss
$= \dfrac{\text{Profit}}{\text{Cost price}} \times 100$	$= \dfrac{\text{Profit}}{\text{Selling price}} \times 100$	$= \dfrac{\text{Loss}}{\text{Cost price}} \times 100$

It is very important for you to be aware of the subtle difference between mark-up and margin.

Example

Rebecca bought a car for €15 880 and sold it for €19 850.
Calculate her profit as a percentage of:

(i) The cost price (mark-up)

(ii) The selling price (margin)

Solution

Profit = 19 850 − 15 880 = €3 970

> **key point**
>
> Profit = Selling price − Cost price

(i) The percentage of cost price = Mark-up

$$= \frac{\text{Profit}}{\text{Cost price}} \times 100$$

$$= \frac{3\,970}{15\,880} \times 100$$

$$= 25\%$$

(ii) The percentage of selling price = Margin

$$= \frac{\text{Profit}}{\text{Selling price}} \times 100$$

$$= \frac{3\,970}{19\,850} \times 100$$

$$= 20\%$$

In some cases the question will ask why the answer to the mark-up is not equal to the margin. The above calculations explain why, i.e. one is over cost price while the other is over selling price.

An importer buys an item for £263·50 sterling when the rate of exchange is €1 = £0·85 sterling. She sells it at a 16% mark-up. Calculate, in euro, the price for which she sells the item.

Solution

Change £263·50 into euro.

Every £0·85 sterling is equal to €1, so we need to see how many times 0·85 divides into 263·50:

$$£0·85 = €1$$

$$£1 = €\frac{1}{0·85}$$

$$£263·50 = \frac{1}{0·85} \times 263·50 = €310$$

Profit is a mark-up of 16%:

$$\text{Profit} = 16\% \text{ of cost price}$$
$$= 16\% \text{ of } €310$$
$$= 0.16 \times 310$$
$$= 49·60$$

$$\text{Selling price} = €310 + €49·60$$
$$= €359·60$$

Here the examiner links currency exchange and percentage mark-up. We expect to see exam questions linking different sections of our course.

Interest

Interest is the sum of money that you pay for borrowing money or that is paid to you for lending money.

A sum of money invested at 10% per annum interest amounts to €907·50 after one year. How much was invested?

key point

Per annum = Per year

Solution

$$100\% = \boxed{\begin{array}{c}\text{Amount} \\ \text{invested}\end{array}} \xrightarrow{+\,10\%} \boxed{907\cdot50} = 110\%$$

We then write 110% = €907·50.

$$1\% = \frac{907\cdot50}{110} \qquad \text{(divide both sides by 110)}$$

$$100\% = \frac{907\cdot50}{110} \times 100 \qquad \text{(multiply both sides by 100)}$$

The amount invested = 100% = €825

Compound interest

The formula for calculating compound interest is given in the booklet of formulae and tables.

$$F = P(1 + i)^t \text{ where } F = \text{Final value}$$
$$P = \text{Principal}$$
$$i = \text{Interest rate}$$
$$t = \text{Number of years}$$

key point

i is always written in decimal form.

$i = 5\% = 0\cdot05$

$i = 16\% = 0\cdot16$

$i = 3\cdot5\% = 0\cdot035,$ etc.

Also the final amount, F, is principal plus interest.

With compound interest, the interest earned each year is added to the principal to form a new principal. This new principal earns interest in the next year and so on.

Method 1:   Use the formula $F = P(1 + i)^t$

Method 2:   Multiply the principal at the beginning of each year by $(1 + i)$. This will give the principal for the next year and so on.

exam focus

The formula is very efficient when combined with a calculator. However, the formula does **not** work if:

(a) The interest rate, i, is changed during the time period or

(b) Money is added or subtracted during the time period.

exam Q

Millie has €3 000 in a special savings account. It has an interest rate of 2·5% per year for 4 years, compounded annually. She does not put any money in or take any money out of the account over the 4 years. Work out the total amount in the account after the 4 years. Give your answer correct to the nearest cent.

Solution

Using the formula, we write:

Given: $P = 3\ 000$ $i = 2·5\% = 0·025$ $t = 4$

$$F = P(1 + i)^t$$
$$F = 3\ 000(1 + 0·025)^4$$
$$F = 3\ 000(1·025)^4$$
$$F = 3\ 311·43867...$$ (using calculator)

At the end of the four years there is €3 311·44 in the account.

key point

The interest rate, i, must be converted into decimal form, by dividing the percentage by 100, before using it in the formula.

Example

Eoin invests €1 000 in the Bank of Rupt.

This bank pays an annual interest rate such that an investment doubles in value every two years.

Eoin thinks that the interest rate must be 50% but his dad, Michael, disagrees. Who is correct? Justify your answer.

Solution

We calculate what €1 000 amounts to in two years at 50% compound interest per annum using the formula:

$F = P(1 + i)^t$

where $P = €1\,000$

$i = 50\% = 0.50$

$t = 2$

Then $F = 1\,000\,(1 + 0.50)^2$

$F = 1\,000\,(1.5)^2 = €2\,250$

Since €2 250 is greater than €2 000 (which is double €1 000), we conclude the interest rate is not 50%. (In fact, the interest rate paid by the bank is less than 50%.)

Michael is correct.

exam focus

Remember, the question does not ask for the interest rate, but to justify whether Eoin or Michael is correct.

exam Q

Dermot has €5 000 and would like to invest it for two years. A special savings account is offering a rate of 3% for the first year and a higher rate for the second year if the money is retained in the account. Tax of 33% will be deducted each year from the interest earned.

(i) How much will the investment be worth at the end of one year, after tax is deducted?

(ii) Dermot calculates that after tax has been deducted, his investment will be worth €5 268 at the end of the second year. Calculate the rate of interest for the second year. Give your answer correct to one decimal place.

Solution

(i) 100% = 5 000

$1\% = \dfrac{5\,000}{100} = 50$

$3\% = 50 \times 3 = €150$

€150 is taxed at 33%

Tax $= \dfrac{150}{100} \times \dfrac{33}{1} = €49.50$

At end of one year the investment

$= 5\,000 + 150 - 49.50$

$= €5\,100.50$

(ii) €5 268 at end of second year − €5 100·50 at end of first year

= €167·50 interest paid after 33% tax.

We write 100% − 33% = 67% = 167·50

$$1\% = \frac{167\cdot50}{67}$$

$$100\% = \frac{167\cdot50 \times 100}{67} = 250$$

Hence, the rate of interest paid for the second year

$$= \frac{\text{Interest paid}}{\text{Principal}} \times 100$$

$$= \frac{250}{5\ 100\cdot50} \times 100$$

$$= 4\cdot90148 \qquad \text{Answer: } 4\cdot9\%$$

Given the final amount

Sometimes we are given the final amount and asked to find the original principal.

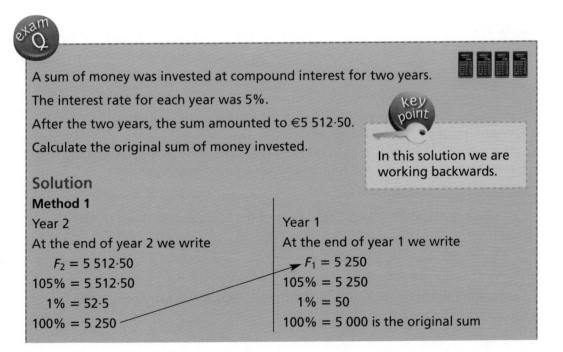

A sum of money was invested at compound interest for two years.

The interest rate for each year was 5%.

After the two years, the sum amounted to €5 512·50.

Calculate the original sum of money invested.

key point

In this solution we are working backwards.

Solution

Method 1

Year 2	Year 1
At the end of year 2 we write	At the end of year 1 we write
$F_2 = 5\ 512\cdot50$	$F_1 = 5\ 250$
105% = 5 512·50	105% = 5 250
1% = 52·5	1% = 50
100% = 5 250	100% = 5 000 is the original sum

Method 2

Using $F = P(1 + i)^t$

where $F = 5\,512{\cdot}50$ and $i = 5\% = 0{\cdot}05$ and $t = 2$

which gives us $\quad 5\,512{\cdot}50 = P(1 + 0{\cdot}05)^2$

$$5\,512{\cdot}50 = P(1{\cdot}05)^2$$

$$5\,512{\cdot}50 = P(1{\cdot}1025)$$

$$\frac{5\,512{\cdot}50}{1{\cdot}1025} = P$$

$$5\,000 = P.$$

or simply use your calculator to solve $5\,512.50 = P(1{\cdot}05)^2$

Depreciation

In some cases the value of an item depreciates (reduces in value) over a period of time.

key point

For depreciation, we use subtraction.

Example

A machine costs €18 500. It depreciated in value by 20% in the first year and by 14% in the second year. Find the value of the machine at the end of two years.

Solution

key point

When calculating depreciation, multiply the value (principal) at the beginning of each year by $(1 - i)$.

This will give the value (principal) for the next year, and so on. Because the rates change each year, the formula cannot be used in this question.

$i = 20\% = 0{\cdot}20$ and $P_1 = 18\,500$, the value of the machine at the start of the first year.

$$1 - i = 1 - 0{\cdot}20 = 0{\cdot}8$$

The value at the end of the first year $= F_1 = 18\,500 \times 0{\cdot}8 = €14\,800$.

For the second year $i = 14\% = 0{\cdot}14$ and $P_2 = 14\,800$, the value of the machine at the start of the second year.

$$1 - i = 1 - 0{\cdot}14 = 0{\cdot}86$$

The value at the end of the second year $= F_2 = 14\,800 \times 0{\cdot}86 = €12\,728$.

Income tax

The following two equations are very important when calculating income tax.

> Gross tax − Tax credits = Tax payable
>
> Net income = Gross income − Tax paid

Net income is also called take-home pay.

You also need to know that gross tax is calculated as follows:

Standard rate on all income up to the standard rate cut-off point	+	A higher rate on all income above the standard rate cut-off point

Deductions on income

All deductions can be divided into two categories: statutory and non-statutory.

Statutory deductions: Compulsory deductions, which must be paid.	**Non-statutory deductions:** Voluntary deductions, which the worker can choose to pay or not pay.
Examples: Income tax Pay-Related Social Insurance (PRSI) Universal Social Charge (USC)	**Examples:** Pension contributions Trade union subscriptions Health insurance payments

Pay-Related Social Insurance (PRSI)

PRSI is made up of social insurance and health contributions.

The amount of PRSI an employee pays depends on how much they earn and is calculated as a percentage of their earnings.

Universal Social Charge (USC)

The Universal Social Charge is an additional tax payable on gross income.

Government budgets

The various rates and bands for PRSI, USC and income tax can be changed in the annual budget.

exam focus

You are not required to learn off USC rates or PRSI bands. If they are required, you will be given them in the question.

Example

A woman has a gross yearly income of €48 000. She has a standard rate cut-off point of €27 500 and a tax credit of €3 852. The standard rate of tax is 18% of income up to the standard rate cut-off point and 37% on all income above the standard rate cut-off point.

Calculate:

(i) The amount of gross tax for the year

(ii) The amount of tax paid for the year

Solution

(i) Gross income: €48 000

Tax is charged as: €27 500 at 18% and 48 000 − 27 500 = €20 500 at 37%

Gross tax = 18% of €27 500 + 37% of €20 500

$\quad\quad\quad = €27\,500 \times 0\cdot18 + €20\,500 \times 0\cdot37$

$\quad\quad\quad = €4\,950 + €7\,585$

$\quad\quad\quad = €12\,535$

(ii) Income tax equation:

Gross tax − Tax credit = Tax payable

€12 535 − €3 852 = €8 683

Therefore, she paid €8 683 in tax.

The table shows the hours Tony worked over five days.

Day	Wednesday	Thursday	Friday	Saturday	Sunday
Hours worked	6	7	7·5	6	h

Tony's basic rate of pay is €13·50 per hour.

He is paid one and a half times the basic rate for work on Saturday and Sunday.

(i) Calculate Tony's total pay for Wednesday, Thursday, Friday and Saturday.

(ii) Tony was paid a total of €540 for the five days' work. Find h, the number of hours Tony worked on Sunday.

(iii) Tony pays income tax at the rate of 20%. He has weekly tax credits of €63. How much income tax does he pay?

(iv) Tony pays the USC at the rate of 2% on the first €193, 4% on the next €115 and 7% on the balance. Calculate the amount of USC Tony pays.

(v) Tony also pays PRSI. His total weekly deductions amount to €76·92. How much PRSI does Tony pay?

Solution

(i) Tony is paid €13·50 per hour for Wednesday, Thursday and Friday.

Tony is paid €13·50 × 1·5 = €20·25 per hour for Saturday and Sunday.

Total pay = (Hours on Wed, Thurs and Fri × €13·50) + (Hours on Sat × €20·25)

$$= ((6 + 7 + 7·5) × €13·50) + (6 × €20·25)$$

$$= (20·5 × €13·50) + (6 × €20·25)$$

$$= €276·75 + €121·50$$

$$= €398·25$$

(ii) Total for five days = (Total for Wed to Sat) + (Total earned on Sunday)

$$€540 = €398·25 + (Total earned on Sunday)$$

$$€141·75 = Total earned on Sunday$$

$$€141·75 = (Hours worked on Sunday × €20·25)$$

$$€141·75 = (h × €20·25)$$

$$7 = h \qquad \text{(divide both sides by €20·25)}$$

Therefore, Tony worked for 7 hours on Sunday.

(iii) Gross tax = 20% of gross wages

$$= (0·2) × €540$$

$$= €108$$

Net tax = Gross tax − Tax credit

Net tax = €108 − €63

Net tax = €45

(iv) USC based on a gross wage of €540:

2% on €193 = € 3·86

4% on €115 = € 4·60

7% on €232 = €16·24 **Note:** 540 − 193 − 115 = 232

Total USC = €24·70

(v) Total deductions = Tax + USC + PRSI

$$€76·92 = €45 + €24·70 + PRSI$$

$$€76·92 = €69·70 + PRSI$$

$$€76·92 − €69·70 = PRSI$$

$$€7·22 = PRSI$$

aims

☐ To become familiar with the four elements of assessment for Junior Cycle Mathematics.

☐ To be familiar with the details of the Classroom-Based Assessment 1.

☐ To be able to understand and apply the Problem-Solving Cycle.

☐ To be familiar with the criteria of quality for assessment.

☐ To understand the four descriptors for the CBA and the criteria associated with each descriptor.

☐ To understand the steps involved in starting your investigation and examining a menu of suggestions for investigation.

☐ To be familiar with the procedure involved with how to carry out a mathematical investigation.

☐ To be able to use the checklist provided to ensure that you haven't missed any key elements in your investigation.

Introduction

As mentioned in the Introduction chapter of this book, your assessment in Junior Cycle Mathematics consists of four elements.

1. **Classroom-Based Assessment 1 (CBA 1)**

   This is a mathematical investigation and it is carried out during your second year of the three-year Junior Cycle. **CBA 1 is covered in this chapter.**

2. **Classroom-Based Assessment 2 (CBA 2)**

   This is a statistical investigation and it is carried out during your third year of the three-year Junior Cycle. **CBA 2 is covered in *Less Stress More Success Maths Book 2.***

3. **Assessment Task**

   This is a written assignment and it is carried out during your third year of the three-year Junior Cycle, after you have completed CBA 2.

4. **Written exam paper**

   This is a 2-hour written exam and it take place at the end of third year, with the rest of your written exams.

CBA 1: Mathematical Investigation

The investigation is an opportunity for you to show that you can apply Mathematics to an area that interests you. Your teacher will give you a timetable and deadline for submitting your investigation.

The details of the investigation are as follows:

Format: A report may be presented in a wide range of formats.

Preparation: A student will, over a three-week period in second year, follow the Problem-Solving Cycle to investigate a mathematical problem.

The Problem-Solving Cycle is as follows:

1. Define a problem
2. Decompose it into manageable parts and/or simplify it using appropriate assumptions
3. Translate the problem to mathematics, if necessary
4. Engage with the problem and solve it, if possible
5. Interpret any findings in the context of the original problem

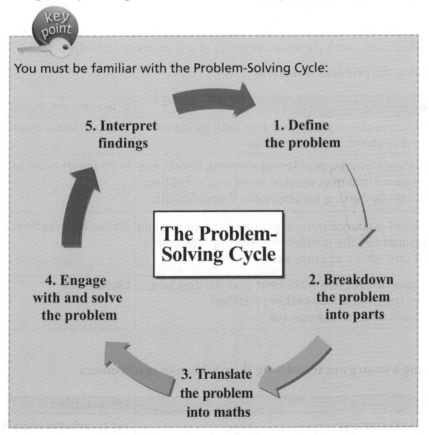

You must be familiar with the Problem-Solving Cycle:

The Problem-Solving Cycle

1. Define the problem
2. Breakdown the problem into parts
3. Translate the problem into maths
4. Engage with and solve the problem
5. Interpret findings

CBA 1: Assessment criteria and four descriptors

The investigation is assessed by the class teacher. A student will be awarded one of the following categories of achievement:

- Yet to meet expectations
- In line with expectations
- Above expectations
- Exceptional

Assessment criteria

A good investigation should be clear and easily understood by one of your fellow classmates (peers) and self-explanatory all of the way through. The criteria are split into four areas A, B, C and D:

 A. Defining the problem statement

 B. Finding a strategy or translating the problem to mathematics

 C. Engaging with the mathematics to solve the problem

 D. Interpreting and reporting

Linking the criteria with the four categories of achievement (descriptors)

A. Defining the problem statement

Criteria	Achievement
Uses a given problem statement and with guidance breaks the problem down into steps	Yet to achieve expectations
With guidance poses a problem statement, breaks the problem down into manageable steps and simplifies the problem by making assumptions, if appropriate	In line with expectations
With limited guidance poses a problem statement and clarifies/simplifies the problem by making reasonable assumptions, where appropriate	Above expectations
Poses a concise problem statement and clarifies and simplifies the problem by making justified assumptions, where appropriate	Exceptional

B. Finding a strategy or translating the problem to mathematics

Criteria	Achievement
Uses a given strategy	Yet to achieve expectations
Chooses an appropriate strategy to engage with the problem	In line with expectations
Justifies the use of a suitable strategy to engage with the problem and identifies any relevant variables	Above expectations
Develops an efficient justified strategy and evaluates progress towards a solution where appropriate; conjectures relationship between variables where appropriate	Exceptional

C. Engaging with the mathematics to solve the problem

Criteria	Achievement
Records some observations/data and follows some basic mathematical procedures	Yet to achieve expectations
Records observations/data and follows suitable mathematical procedures with minor errors; graphs and/or diagrams/words are used to provide insights into the problem and/or solution	In line with expectations
Records observations/data systematically, suitable mathematical procedures are followed, and accurate mathematical language, symbolic notation and visual representations are used; attempts are made to generalise any observed patterns in the solution/observation	Above expectations
Mathematical procedures are followed with a high level of precision, and a justified answer is achieved; solution/observations are generalised and extended to other situations where appropriate	Exceptional

D. Interpreting and reporting

Criteria	Achievement
Comments on any solution	Yet to achieve expectations
Comments on the reasonableness of the solution where appropriate and makes a concrete connection to the original question, uses everyday familiar language to communicate ideas	In line with expectations
Checks reasonableness of solution and revisits assumptions and/or strategy to iterate the process, if necessary, uses formal mathematical language to communicate ideas and identifies what worked well and what could be improved	Above expectations
Deductive arguments used and precise mathematical language and symbolic notation used to consolidate mathematical thinking and justify decisions and solutions; strengths and/or weaknesses in the mathematical representation/solution strategy are identified	Exceptional

Academic honesty

Academic honesty means that your work is based on your own original ideas and not copied from other people. However, you may draw on the work and ideas of others, but this must be acknowledged. This would be put into a reference list at the end of your investigation, known as a bibliography. In addition, you should use your own language and expression.

Record-keeping

Throughout the investigation, keep a journal, either on paper or online. This journal will also help you to demonstrate academic honesty. The journal will be of great assistance in focusing your efforts when writing your CBA 1 investigation.

- Make notes of any websites or books you use.
- You are encouraged to use a variety of support materials and present your work in a variety of formats.
- Keep a record of your actions so you can show your teacher how much time you are spending on your investigation.
- Remember to follow your teacher's advice and meet your CBA 1 timetable.
- The teacher is there to facilitate you, so do not be afraid to ask for guidance. The more focused your questions are, the better guidance your teacher can give you.

Evidence of learning

The following evidence is required

- A report
- Student research records

You must report your research and findings in a format of your choice. The report can be completed at the end of the investigation. If a typed or hand-written report is the format of choice, the total length of the report would typically be in the 400–600 words range (excluding tables, graphs, reference list and research records), but this should not be regarded as a rigid requirement.

Choosing a topic

You should choose a topic that you are interested in, because then you will be inclined to put more effort into the project. In addition, you will enjoy working on your project and this will shine through. You should discuss the topic with your teacher before you put too much time and effort into it, in case your idea is not in line with what a mathematical investigation should be.

If you cannot think of a topic yourself, then you can ask your teacher for help in coming up with a topic to investigate. Below are some ideas that might help you to come up with an investigation of your own.

Suggestions for investigation, with ideas to consider:

- Investigating the cost of a family weekend in a foreign city
  - Destination
  - Transportation
  - Hotel
  - Currency exchange
  - Activities
- Garden design
  - Size, shape and dimensions of garden
  - Features: flower bed/pond/trees/patio
  - Draw a sketch
  - Work out costs
- Bedroom makeover
  - Carpet/wooden floor
  - Walls painted or wallpapered
  - Furniture – bed/desk/wardrobe
  - Decoration
  - Work out costs
- Best placement of security sensors in different shaped rooms
  - Radius of detection on the average sensor
  - Best placement in a rectangular room/square room/L-shaped room
- An environmental investigation. For example, glass recycling
  - Mass of glass per bottle bank
  - How often the bank is emptied
  - Average mass of glass recycled per household

- Traffic study at an airport or local train station
  - o Number of cars in and out daily
  - o Number of foot passengers passing through
  - o Number of airplanes/trains arriving and departing daily
  - o Peak times?
- Budgeting for a 'Debs ball' for a couple
  - o Cost of dress/suit hire
  - o Beauty treatments – tan, nails, makeup, haircuts
  - o Transport to and from the venue
  - o Spending money
- Cost of installing solar panels in a house and expected savings in energy and environmental costs
  - o Cost of annual electricity bill
  - o Cost of installing solar panels
  - o Amount of energy generated
  - o Annual savings
- Public transport costs and car usage: A personal comparison
  - o Annual cost of running a car – insurance, tax, depreciation
  - o Petrol costs
  - o Bus/train/taxi use for equivalent journeys
- Mapping the path of a diver jumping from a board into water
  - o Video record a diver/observe a video
  - o Using a point of reference, note down the height of the diver after every 0.1 of a second
  - o Graph results. Observe shape
- Investigate the potential profit that can be made from buying ingredients and baking cupcakes for a school cake sale
  - o How many cupcakes will you make?
  - o Ingredients needed and cost of same
  - o Selling price of cupcakes
  - o Profit?
- Using a map of your local area, design a 10 km fun-run route. Use average speeds of walkers and runners to work out how long the route should be closed for, to allow the run to take place
  - o Look at a map of the local area and look at different options for a route
  - o One single route or a 5 km route that is done twice?
  - o Is there a route that will cause least disruption? Park/road/country lanes?

- Investigate which electricity energy provider is offering the best deal at the moment, for an average family home
    - o Average annual usage of electricity
    - o Compare cost of electricity from various suppliers
- Investigate the cost of pet ownership
    - o Initial cost of getting a pet
    - o Equipment (bed/toys/fish tank)
    - o Annual cost of food and treats
    - o Vet visits
    - o Kennelling/cattery costs while on holiday
- Investigate fitness programmes for muscle building or calorie burning
    - o Compare various workout routines – aerobics/cardio/weight-lifting
    - o Time spent on a regime
- Investigate the breakdown of how teenagers spend their money
    - o Sources of income – pocket money/part-time job/gifts
    - o Breakdown of expenditure

Getting started

Once you have chosen your investigation, the next step is to do some research. The purpose of this research is to determine the suitability of your investigation. Do not limit your research to the internet. Your local or school library will have books on mathematics that are interesting and may be useful.

The following questions may help you decide if your chosen investigation is suitable:

- What area of mathematics are contained in my investigation?
- Can I understand and use the mathematics required?
- Can I define a precise problem statement related to this topic?
- Am I totally familiar with the problem-solving cycle?
- Have I clearly defined the problem statement?
- How can I show the work I did, as part of my investigation?
- Can I limit my work to the 400–600 word range report (excluding tables, graphs, reference list, bibliography and research records) if I choose this investigation?

If your original investigation is not suitable, has your research suggested another, better investigation? Otherwise, could you either narrow down or widen out your investigation to make it suitable?

Once you think you have a workable investigation, then you must start into the Problem-Solving Cycle by carrying out the following steps:

A. Define the problem
B. Translate the problem to mathematics
C. Engage with the mathematics to solve the problem
D. Interpret and report your findings

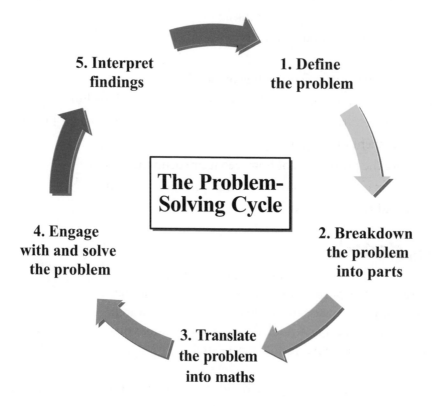

Now you are ready to start writing your investigation in detail.

Remember that your peers (fellow students) should be able to read and understand your investigation.

The following table, designed to support teachers in giving feedback to their students, will help you when carrying out each step of your investigation.

Area of Activity	Questions to focus on during formative feedback	Vocabulary to build
Defining the problem	What is the big problem that you are trying to investigate/solve? Does it have more than one possible answer?	Open-ended problem Constraints
Defining the problem	What is the specific problem your mathematical representation is going to investigate/solve? What elements are you going to focus on during your investigation?	Specific, focus
Translating to Mathematics (if necessary)	What ideas did you think about that you decided not to try?	Eliminate, prioritise
Translating to Mathematics (if necessary)	What have you assumed in order to investigate/solve the problem? Why did you make these choices?	Assumptions
Translating to Mathematics (if necessary)	What qualities are important? Which ones change and which ones stay the same?	Variables
Engaging with the problem and solving it if possible	Where did you find the numbers that you used?	Research
Engaging with the problem and solving it if possible	What pictures, diagrams or graphs might help people understand your information, mathematical representation and results?	Diagrams, graphs, tables
Engaging with the problem and solving it if possible	What mathematical ideas did you use to describe the situation and solve your problem?	Mathematical ideas

Area of Activity	Questions to focus on during formative feedback	Vocabulary to build
Interpreting the solution	How do you know that your calculations are correct? Did you remember to use units €, cm, etc.?	Calculation, unit
Interpreting the solution	When does your mathematical representation work? When do you need to be careful because it might not?	Limitations
Interpreting the solution	How do you know that you have a good useful mathematical representation? Why does your representation make sense?	Testing, validation
Interpreting the solution	Could you do anything to make your mathematical representation better or more accurate?	Improvement, iteration
Communicating/ Reporting results	Explain your representation in words and mathematical notation	Mathematical notation
Communicating/ Reporting results	How did each of your teammates help?	Collaboration
Communicating/ Reporting results	What are the most important things for your audience to understand about your mathematical representation and/or solution?	Audience

Source www.ncca.ie

Mindmap for CBA

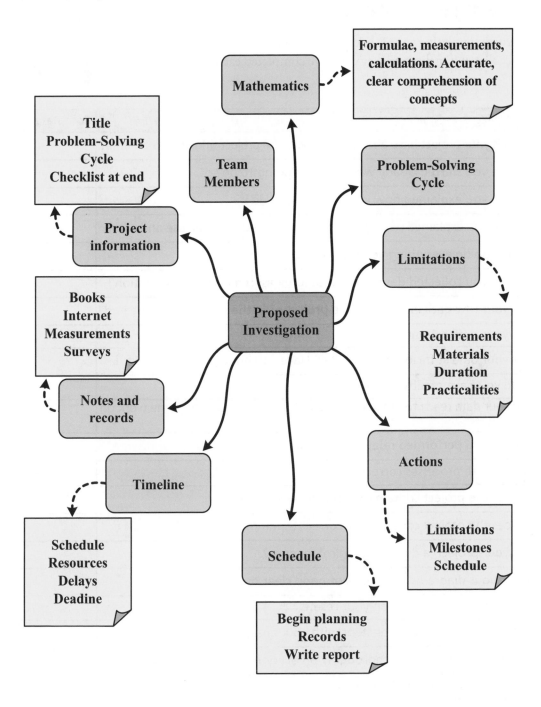

Classroom-Based Assessment Investigation Checklist

Before completing your CBA, go through the following checklist and make sure that you have completed each task.

Activity	Completed?
Does your project have a front cover with the project title and your name?	
Have you started clearly what you are going to do?	
Have you explained how you are going to do it?	
Have you explained what mathematical methods you will use and why?	
Did you do everything you said you would do?	
Have you collected data or generated measurements or information?	
Is your raw data included in the project or in the appendix, at the end?	
Is your data relevant?	
Is your data sufficient in quantity? Have you enough data?	
Do you have quality data?	
Is your data ready to use immediately, or do you need to do some work on it first?	
Have you performed relevant mathematical processes?	
Are these processes correct?	
Does the project contain only correct notation?	
Does the project contain only correct terminology?	
Is your project laid out in a logical manner?	
Are your diagrams and tables of good clear quality?	
Have you commented on your results?	
Are your comments consistent with your analysis?	
Have you commented thoroughly on everything that you have done?	
Have you commented on validity?	
Do you have an appendix, if one is needed?	
Do you have a bibliography?	